D0944105

DUE DATE

PRENTICE-HALL CONTEMPORARY

PERSPECTIVES IN PHILOSOPHY SERIES

Joel Feinberg and Wesley C. Salmon, *editors*

Alan Ross Anderson	MINDS AND MACHINES
John V. Canfield	PURPOSE IN NATURE
V. C. Chappell	ORDINARY LANGUAGE
Nelson Pike	GOD AND EVIL
George Pitcher	TRUTH
Vincent Tomas	CREATIVITY IN THE ARTS

PURPOSE IN NATURE

Edited by

JOHN V. CANFIELD

Cornell University

CONTEMPORARY PERSPECTIVES
IN PHILOSOPHY SERIES

PRENTICE-HALL, INC. Englewood Cliffs, New Jersey

PRENTICE-HALL INTERNATIONAL, INC., *London*
PRENTICE-HALL OF AUSTRALIA, PTY. LTD., *Sydney*
PRENTICE-HALL OF CANADA, LTD., *Toronto*
PRENTICE-HALL OF INDIA (PRIVATE) LTD., *New Delhi*
PRENTICE-HALL OF JAPAN, INC., *Tokyo*

© 1966
by PRENTICE-HALL, INC.
Englewood Cliffs, N.J.

Current printing (last digit) :

10   9   8   7   6   5   4   3   2   1

Library of Congress Catalog Card Number:
66-18159

Printed in the United States of America

C-74271

CONTEMPORARY PERSPECTIVES

IN PHILOSOPHY

This series is designed to provide a wide group of readers with collections of essays by contemporary philosophers on problems presently under active discussion in philosophical circles. The articles have been carefully selected for their lucidity and intelligibility, revealing the vitality of current philosophy to an audience which would not normally have recourse to professional journals. Each volume consists of articles devoted to a single topic, thereby creating an unusual degree of internal coherence and dialectical unity. In many cases the articles are addressed to one another as replies or rebuttals, or are otherwise built upon earlier essays to carry the discussion forward to new levels of clarity. The editor of each volume contributes an introduction which furnishes the reader with the orientation and general framework for a full understanding of the issues. Although each volume is deliberately restricted in scope, the series as a whole ranges over the entire breadth of philosophy, from aesthetics and philosophy of religion to semantics and philosophy of science.

The series is dedicated to the view that contemporary philosophical perspectives—even on ancient problems—are distinctive, exciting, and fully intelligible to students and other nonprofessionals. The volumes are designed for use as supplementary materials or as components in larger "homemade" anthologies, in both introductory and advanced courses, and for use as basic source materials for student research projects. They enable the teacher to expose students to current philosophy without the usual struggle over library copies of journals. In addition, these anthologies will be useful to scholars in fields bordering on philosophy—for example, law, linguistics, literature, mathematics, physics, psychology, and theology—who wish to find in convenient capsule form the best of recent philosophical thinking on subjects of interest to them. For readers in general, the series provides an opportunity to sample the actual substance and methods of contemporary philosophy.

JOEL FEINBERG
Princeton University

WESLEY C. SALMON
Indiana University

CONTENTS

INTRODUCTION
John V. Canfield
1

BEHAVIOR, PURPOSE, AND TELEOLOGY
Arturo Rosenblueth,
Norbert Wiener,
and *Julian Bigelow*
9

COMMENTS ON A MECHANISTIC CONCEPTION
OF PURPOSEFULNESS
Richard Taylor
17

CAUSAL AND TELEOLOGICAL EXPLANATION
Richard D. Braithwaite
27

THOUGHTS ON TELEOLOGY
Israel Scheffler
48

TELEOLOGICAL EXPLANATION
Ernest Nagel
67

THE LOGIC OF FUNCTIONAL ANALYSIS
Carl G. Hempel
89

SELECTED BIBLIOGRAPHY
109

PURPOSE IN NATURE

INTRODUCTION

JOHN V. CANFIELD

In the *Metaphysics* Aristotle writes: "When one man said, then, that reason was present—as in animals, so throughout nature—as the cause of order and all arrangement, he seemed like a sober man in contrast with the random talk of his predecessors." To tough-minded people today it would be rather the man who *denies* the appropriateness of a teleological interpretation of nature who would appear sober. In the present scientific climate we would press an objection Aristotle foresaw and tried to refute: "Why should not nature work, not for the sake of something, nor because it is better so, but as the sky rains, not in order to make the corn grow, but of necessity?"

The controversy about purpose in nature illustrated in these quotations involves a number of important and as yet unsolved problems. Some of these problems interest the practicing scientist as well as the philosopher. The scientist, in particular the biologist, is concerned with problems of methodology connected with purpose and teleology. He wants to know what kinds of explanatory concepts are legitimate to use, and is worried about the import of some of those concepts which he does use, though reluctantly. The same problems of method occur

1

again in a slightly different form in the philosophy of science. The metaphysician, looking at the controversy from a still different point of view, sees in it fundamental issues about the nature of the world.

Before enumerating some of these problems and commenting on the discussions of them contained in the selections in this book, I will mention briefly some views about purpose in nature which were once widely held.

In the past, the order and regularity of the movements of the stars and planets seemed to many an indication of design, or planning. Where we observe design and planning, it is natural to suppose a planner; and it is a natural extension of this idea to explain the existence of the universe itself in terms of the aims or purposes of the planner. We can explain the existence of a water wheel, for example, in terms of the purpose of the person who made it. Exactly the same kind of explanation can be given for the existence of the universe, on the supposition that it was created for a purpose. Furthermore, animate nature, even more than inanimate, seems to show evidence of the work of an artificer. In the first place, human and other animal bodies seem well thought out and well executed contrivances. Consider, for example, the complicated machinery of the eye. It is hard to imagine that such a complex structure, so well adapted to its ends, could have come into being by accident rather than design. Furthermore, the interdependence of different species of animals has been viewed as the work of a planner. One can think of plants as designed to serve the purpose of nourishing animals, and of animals, in turn, as designed to serve the purpose of nourishing man. The Stoic Chrysipus, for example, thought that the pig exists only in order to serve man as food, and that its soul was given it in the place of salt, in order to preserve its flesh for us.

Modern science, of course, disavows teleological explanations of this kind. At the same time, however, some of the key expressions used in stating such teleological explanations occur regularly in biology as well as in our everyday talk about the behavior of animals. These expressions include "purpose," "function," "role," and "in order to," and occur in such sentences about the parts of animals as: "A function of the liver is to secrete bile"; "The heart beats in order to circulate the blood"; and "The role of the sodium chloride is to prevent the cells from taking up too much water." It is usual also to speak of animals as acting for or with a purpose. The biologist typically makes such claims as: "Brooding birds possess a territory for the purpose of preserving the species."

What is the point of such teleological language? If the world is the creation of a designer, the language has a point and is appropriate. Discussion of the role or purpose of a part of a machine takes its point from the fact that the part was designed by someone to do something. But science abjures explicit or implicit reliance on the corresponding assumption that the world and its parts were designed. Is teleological language therefore vestigial, a metaphorical way of speaking which can in principle be dispensed with?

Some may think that this question about language can be settled by appealing to the facts. The relevant facts include the following: first, the parts of living things seem to be interrelated in much the same way as the parts of machines, in that they work together to achieve a goal, namely, the survival of the individual and its species; second, the living things themselves engage in complicated behavior which seems purposive, such as birds building elaborate nests to house their as yet unborn young.

These facts, together with facts about such seemingly mysterious phenomena as regeneration, have in the past led some biologists to say, for example, that cells act with a purpose. Some have even been led to the hypostatization of a mysterious biological entity, the entelechy, to account for the seeming purposiveness of the phenomena.

On the other hand, the accepted opinion is that the above facts can be explained by appealing to evolutionary theory. The purpose we seem to see in the interrelations of the parts of living things and in their behavior is merely the result of evolution. All the facts can, at least in principle, be explained by appealing to the laws of genetics and to the process of natural selection. The biological phenomena can thus be given a naturalistic explanation, and the notion of purpose is superfluous.

If this is so, we should be able to do two things. First, we should be able, at least in principle, to translate every teleological sentence (that is, every sentence using a teleological term such as "purpose") into a nonteleological one. The problem then is: what is the correct translation? Second, we should be able to account for the explanatory force of teleological sentences without appealing to teleological notions. Let us examine these problems in more detail.

The first problem has been recently discussed with respect to the word "function," which occurs in sentences about the workings of parts of plants and animals. It is an important task in physiology to discover the functions of the various organs and biological entities. Investigators are currently trying to discover the functions of the thymus, for example. "Function" is a teleological word, closely related to "role" and "purpose." Can all sentences containing "function" be translated into sentences which contain neither "function" nor any other teleological term? A positive answer here is a necessary condition for a positive answer to the question about the translatability of teleological sentences in general. If the translation cannot be made, and if we are thus forced to retain a teleological word in our descriptions of nature, it would seem that there is something inherently teleological in the facts about which we are speaking.

If the problem of translatability is answered in the negative, biology, the science of life, will differ radically from physics and chemistry, since the latter two have no need for teleological sentences or terms. Thus a puzzling discontinuity will exist between the physical and the life sciences. The same point can be put by speaking of the unity of science and of the possibilities of a reduction of biology to the physical sciences. It has been thought that everything we would want to say in biology using such biological concepts as "cell" can in principle be said in sentences using only the concepts, for example, of physics. But if biology contains sentences which cannot be translated into nonteleological ones, the proposed reduction is impossible, and thus the "mechanistic" metaphysics proves unable to deal with the phenomena of life studied in biology.

One might think that a simple translation of function sentences is possible. It has been claimed, for example, that "The function of the heart is to circulate the blood," means simply that the heart circulates the blood and that in general the word "function" is simply superfluous. But as Hempel will point out, if this thesis were true, it would be true (but obviously is not) that a function of the heart is to produce heart sounds, since the heart does produce heart sounds. Thus this simple solution fails; and in fact the problem of providing a translation has proven to be very difficult.

The first essay, the widely influential article by Arturo Rosenblueth, Norbert Wiener, and Julian Bigelow, may be viewed as, in part, an early attempt to provide a translation schema for teleological sentences. The authors' guiding idea seems to be this. It is possible to compare animals to machines, stressing the fact (if it is one) that machines can be understood in purely mechanistic terms. This leads to the view that the notion of purpose is unnecessary in describing animals. Wiener and his associates make the same comparison between animals and machines, but the machines they have in mind are those (such as an antimissile missile) which seek a goal and which attain the goal even though the goal attempts to elude them, and even though the circumstances in which they seek it vary. The machines are guided by negative feedback from the goal object, and their behavior is self-correcting. It is tempting to say that these machines have a purpose, and to try to understand the purposive behavior of animals in terms of these machines—that is, in terms of negative feedback. Since these purposive machines, like all machines, can presumably be understood mechanistically, the same will be true of the behavior of animals.

The essays by Richard Braithwaite and Ernest Nagel may also be viewed as attempts to provide a schema for translating all teleological sentences into sentences which contain no teleological terms.

Attempts to translate teleology out of biology seem to fall into one of two patterns. Either the system of translation is a *target* schema, or it is a *furnace* schema. Those who construct target schemata take as their guiding examples such instances of teleological behavior as a cat chasing a mouse, or, on the mechanistic side, a homing torpedo proceeding to its goal. Furnace schemata, on the other hand, are modeled after a different kind of teleological behavior, namely, that exemplified by a house equipped with an automatic furnace. This schema best fits such biological behavior as the homeostasis of temperature and of blood sugar.

Braithwaite offers a target schema, though he claims that his analysis works also for the furnacelike cases. Nagel, on the other hand, offers a model evidently designed on the furnace pattern. In both essays a translation schema is worked out carefully and in detail.

The article by Richard Taylor is a valuable criticism of the paper by Wiener and his associates. Taylor raises problems which must be met by later attempts to provide a translation schema. Israel Scheffler, in the critical part of his article "Thoughts on Teleology," reiterates some of Taylor's criticisms and adds several new ones, addressing himself to Wiener's paper and to Braithwaite's. No criticisms of Nagel's article are included here. It is interesting to consider whether he avoids the kinds of counterexamples produced by Taylor and Scheffler.

The second problem involved in the controversy over purpose in nature centers on teleological sentences which serve, or purport to serve, as *explanations*. In some contexts a teleological sentence seems to provide an appropriate answer to a request for an explanation. For example: "Why does the heart beat?" "In order to circulate the blood." The fact that in the right context the latter sentence seems to provide an explanation of the heartbeat raises several problems. First, what, exactly, is being explained in this and similar cases? The answer is, it would seem: the existence and persistence in the species in question of the part, organ, or piece of behavior in question. That is, what is being explained is how the part or behavior pattern came to develop and persist in the species. But giving such an explanation is a great deal for a single sentence of the above kind to accomplish. How, then, does the sentence provide an explanation? What is the source of its explanatory power?

There is a widespread view in the philosophy of science that an explanation of something consists of an *argument* which is such that from the premises of the argument a statement of what is being explained follows either deductively or inductively. The premises must contain laws, and the explanation proceeds, in effect, by subsuming the thing being explained under these laws. This view is known as the covering-law model of explanation.

Hempel and Nagel both presuppose the correctness of the covering-law model, both having defended it elsewhere. At first glance this presupposition is hard to reconcile with the existence of teleological explanations consisting of *single sentences*. To fit this fact to the model, such sentences must be treated as elliptical arguments, and must be unpacked into premises and conclusion, with the premises containing true lawlike generalizations.

Both Nagel and Hempel provide such an unpacking. Because the solution thus attempted to the problem of the explanatory force of teleological sentences involves a translation of the sentences, it is easy to confuse the problem of explanation with the problem of translation already discussed; however, the two problems are separate. One involves the meaning of certain kinds of sentences, the other involves the explanatory force these sentences have in virtue of their meaning. Because a solution to the first problem must take into account the phenomena which lead to the second problem, and because on some views an answer to the first problem provides an automatic answer to the second, does not mean that the two problems are one.

Although Nagel and Hempel agree on their general approach to the problem of explanation, they disagree on its solution. For Hempel, teleological "explanations" are would-be covering-law explanations that for the most part fail to explain what they attempt to explain. For Nagel, on the contrary, they succeed. Part of the issue here concerns whether or not it is true that the function of something is to do X only if the presence of the thing in question is *necessary* for the doing of X. This question depends partly on the meaning of the word "necessary" as it is used here.

Since Nagel's work on teleology has centered on the development of a model for goal-directed behavior, a few words about the model will be useful. As presented in this anthology, the motivation for the development of the model is as follows. Nagel first provides an analysis of teleological sentences in biology into arguments which fit the covering-law model. He then points out difficulties with this analysis. The model is presented as a way of meeting the difficulties. There is, however, no extended discussion of exactly how the model is to be employed to meet the difficulties, and the reader will want to pursue this question.

The work of both Hempel and Nagel on teleological explanation might be seen in better perspective if, in conclusion, I mention two possible alternative approaches to the problem. First, one might hold that the supposition that all scientific explanation fits the covering-law model is best treated as an open question, and that teleological explanation should be approached free of the supposition. Possibly so-called teleological explanation in biology is both *sui generis* (non–covering-law model) and scientifically respectable.

The second alternative approach is related to the first. Perhaps teleological sentences provide explanations only against the background of some theory. In the past this theory was some form of theism. At present, evolutionary theory forms the background against which teleological sentences achieve explanatory force. On this view, the explanatory force of the sentences is to be sought, not by unpacking them into arguments, but by relating them to this background. For every part of every species, and for every characteristic behavior pattern, evolutionary theory provides an incomplete sketch or outline both of how that part or behavior pattern developed in the species and of how it came to persist. By sketch or outline, I mean to indicate two things: first, that most of the details will not be filled in, and most we will never be able to fill in. The geological record provides totally inadequate evidence about the structure of the soft parts of species at crucial points in their evolution, their behavior patterns, the content of the gene pool at a given time, and so on. Second, without some of these details we will not be sure that certain parts and behavior patterns have an evolutionary explanation of the usual kind. It might be, for example, that a given biological entity is genetically linked to an adaptive change in some other part of the organism, and is itself not adaptive. What teleological sentences do, from the present view, is to fill in an important part of the sketch. They tell us what a biological entity does that is useful to the individual or the species. In this way they provide an explanation, given the truth of evolutionary theory, and given that we suppose that there is some correct way (not necessarily known to us) of filling in the remaining details in the explanatory sketch. Without the assumption that the entity does something useful for the animal or species, we do not have the necessary beginning of an evolutionary account of the entity's development. *With* this information, however, evolutionary theory tells us what kind of events must have led to the development of the entity and to its persistence in the species. That we do not have the full story even then seems not by itself to rule out the claim that we have explained the existence of the entity.

In this introduction I have tried to clarify two of the problems involved in the controversy over purpose in nature, and to relate to these issues the discussions contained in the essays reprinted here. Many other issues are involved in the controversy. Like most philosophical controversies, it tends, when examined closely, to resolve itself into difficult and fundamental issues, such as, in this case, questions about the nature of cause, purpose, and explanation. The essays included here provide, I believe, a rich source for philosophical inquiry.

BEHAVIOR, PURPOSE, AND TELEOLOGY

ARTURO ROSENBLUETH, NORBERT WIENER,
AND JULIAN BIGELOW

This essay has two goals. The first is to define the behavioristic study of natural events and to classify behavior. The second is to stress the importance of the concept of purpose.

Given any object, relatively abstracted from its surroundings for study, the behavioristic approach consists in the examination of the output of the object and of the relations of this output to the input. By output is meant any change produced in the surroundings by the object. By input, conversely, is meant any event external to the object that modifies this object in any manner.

The above statement of what is meant by the behavioristic method of study omits the specific structure and the intrinsic organization of the object. This omission is fundamental because on it is based the distinction between the behavioristic and the alternative functional method of study. In a functional analysis, as opposed to a behavioristic approach, the main goal is the intrinsic organization of the entity studied, its structure and its properties; the relations between the object and the surroundings are relatively incidental.

"Behavior, Purpose, and Teleology," Philosophy of Science, Vol. X, No. 1 (January, 1943), pp. 18-24. Copyright © 1943. The Williams & Wilkins Co., Baltimore 2, Md., U.S.A.

From this definition of the behavioristic method a broad definition of behavior ensues. By behavior is meant any change of an entity with respect to its surroundings. This change may be largely an output from the object, the input being then minimal, remote, or irrelevant; or else the change may be immediately traceable to a certain input. Accordingly, any modification of an object, detectable externally, may be denoted as behavior. The term would be, therefore, too extensive for usefulness were it not that it may be restricted by apposite adjectives— that is, that behavior may be classified.

The consideration of the changes of energy involved in behavior affords a basis for classification. Active behavior is that in which the object is the source of the output energy involved in a given specific reaction. The object may store energy supplied by a remote or relatively immediate input, but the input does not energize the output directly. In passive behavior, on the contrary, the object is not a source of energy; all the energy in the output can be traced to the immediate input (for example, the throwing of an object), or else the object may control energy which remains external to it throughout the reaction (for example, the soaring flight of a bird).

Active behavior may be subdivided into two classes: purposeless (or random) and purposeful. The term "purposeful" is meant to denote that the act or behavior may be interpreted as directed to the attainment of a goal—that is, to a final condition in which the behaving object reaches a definite correlation in time or in space with respect to another object or event. Purposeless behavior, then, is that which is not interpreted as directed to a goal.

The vagueness of the words "may be interpreted" as used above might be considered so great that the distinction would be useless. Yet the recognition that behavior may sometimes be purposeful is unavoidable and useful, as follows. The basis of the concept of purpose is the awareness of "voluntary activity." Now, the purpose of voluntary acts is not a matter of arbitrary interpretation but a physiological fact. When we perform a voluntary action what we select voluntarily is a specific purpose, not a specific movement. Thus, if we decide to take a glass containing water and carry it to our mouth we do not command certain muscles to contract to a certain degree and in a certain sequence; we merely trip the purpose and the reaction follows automatically. Indeed, experimental physiology has so far been largely incapable of explaining the mechanism of voluntary activity. We submit that this failure is due to the fact that when an experimenter stimulates the motor regions of the cerebral cortex he does not duplicate a voluntary reaction; he trips efferent, "output" pathways, but does not trip a purpose, as is done voluntarily.

The view has often been expressed that all machines are purposeful.

This view is untenable. First may be mentioned mechanical devices such as a roulette, designed precisely for purposelessness. Then may be considered devices such as a clock, designed, it is true, with a purpose, but having a performance which, although orderly, is not purposeful— that is, there is no specific final condition toward which the movement of the clock strives. Similarly, although a gun may be used for a definite purpose, the attainment of a goal is not intrinsic to the performance of the gun; random shooting can be made, deliberately purposeless.

Some machines, on the other hand, are intrinsically purposeful. A torpedo with a target-seeking mechanism is an example. The term "servomechanisms" has been coined precisely to designate machines with intrinsic purposeful behavior.

It is apparent from these considerations that although the definition of purposeful behavior is relatively vague, and hence operationally largely meaningless, the concept of purpose is useful and should, therefore, be retained.

Purposeful active behavior may be subdivided into two classes: "feedback" (or "teleological") and "nonfeedback" (or "nonteleological"). The expression "feedback" is used by engineers in two different senses. In a broad sense it may denote that some of the output energy of an apparatus or machine is returned as input; as example is an electrical amplifier with feedback. The feedback is in these cases positive—the fraction of the output which re-enters the object has the same sign as the original input signal. Positive feedback adds to the input signals, it does not correct them. The term "feedback" is also employed in a more restricted sense to signify that the behavior of an object is controlled by the margin of error at which the object stands at a given time with reference to a relatively specific goal. The feedback is then negative, that is, the signals from the goal are used to restrict outputs which would otherwise go beyond the goal. It is this second meaning of the term "feedback" that is used here.

All purposeful behavior may be considered to require negative feedback. If a goal is to be attained, some signals from the goal are necessary at some time to direct the behavior. By nonfeedback behavior is meant that in which there are no signals from the goal which modify the activity of the object *in the course of the behavior*. Thus, a machine may be set to impinge upon a luminous object although the machine may be insensitive to light. Similarly, a snake may strike at a frog, or a frog at a fly, with no visual or other report from the prey after the movement has started. Indeed, the movement is in these cases so fast that it is not likely that nerve impulses would have time to arise at the retina, travel to the central nervous system and set up further impulses which would reach the muscles in time to modify the movement effectively.

As opposed to the examples considered, the behavior of some machines and some reactions of living organisms involve a continuous feedback from the goal that modifies and guides the behaving object. This type of behavior is more effective than that mentioned above, particularly when the goal is not stationary. But continuous feedback control may lead to very clumsy behavior if the feedback is inadequately damped and becomes therefore positive instead of negative for certain frequencies of oscillation. Suppose, for example, that a machine is designed with the purpose of impinging upon a moving luminous goal; the path followed by the machine is controlled by the direction and intensity of the light from the goal. Suppose further that the machine overshoots seriously when it follows a movement of the goal in a certain direction; an even stronger stimulus will then be delivered which will turn the machine in the opposite direction. If that movement again overshoots a series of increasingly larger oscillations will ensue and the machine will miss the goal.

This picture of the consequences of undamped feedback is strikingly similar to that seen during the performance of a voluntary act by a cerebellar patient. At rest the subject exhibits no obvious motor disturbance. If he is asked to carry a glass of water from a table to his mouth, however, the hand carrying the glass will execute a series of oscillatory motions of increasing amplitude as the glass approaches his mouth, so that the water will spill and the purpose will not be fulfilled. This test is typical of the disorderly motor performance of patients with cerebellar disease. The analogy with the behavior of a machine with undamped feedback is so vivid that we venture to suggest that the main function of the cerebellum is the control of the feedback nervous mechanisms involved in purposeful motor activity.

Feedback purposeful behavior may again be subdivided. It may be extrapolative (predictive), or it may be nonextrapolative (nonpredictive). The reactions of unicellular organisms known as tropisms are examples of nonpredictive performances. The amoeba merely follows the source to which it reacts; there is no evidence that it extrapolates the path of a moving source. Predictive animal behavior, on the other hand, is a commonplace. A cat starting to pursue a running mouse does not run directly toward the region where the mouse is at any given time, but moves toward an extrapolated future position. Examples of both predictive and nonpredictive servomechanisms may also be found readily.

Predictive behavior may be subdivided into different orders. The cat chasing the mouse is an instance of first-order prediction; the cat merely predicts the path of the mouse. Throwing a stone at a moving target requires a second-order prediction; the paths of the target and of the stone should be foreseen. Examples of predictions of higher order are shooting with a sling or with a bow and arrow.

Predictive behavior requires the discrimination of at least two co-ordinates, a temporal and at least one spatial axis. Prediction will be more effective and flexible, however, if the behaving object can respond to changes in more than one spatial coordinate. The sensory receptors of an organism, or the corresponding elements of a machine, may therefore limit the predictive behavior. Thus, a bloodhound *follows* a trail, that is, it does not show any predictive behavior in trailing, because a chemi-cal, olfactory input reports only spatial information: distance, as in-dicated by intensity. The external changes capable of affecting auditory, or, even better, visual receptors, permit more accurate spatial localiza-tion; hence the possibility of more effective predictive reactions when the input affects those receptors.

In addition to the limitations imposed by the receptors upon the ability to perform extrapolative actions, limitations may also occur that are due to the internal organization of the behaving object. Thus, a machine which is to trail predictively a moving luminous object should not only be sensitive to light (for example, by the possession of a photoelectric cell), but should also have the structure adequate for interpreting the luminous input. It is probable that limitations of in-ternal organization, particularly of the organization of the central nervous system, determine the complexity of predictive behavior which a mammal may attain. Thus, it is likely that the nervous system of a rat or dog is such that it does not permit the integration of input and output necessary for the performance of a predictive reaction of the third or fourth order. Indeed, it is possible that one of the features of the discontinuity of behavior observable when comparing humans with other high mammals may lie in that the other mammals are limited to predictive behavior of a low order, whereas man may be capable poten-tially of quite high orders of prediction.

The classification of behavior suggested so far is tabulated here:

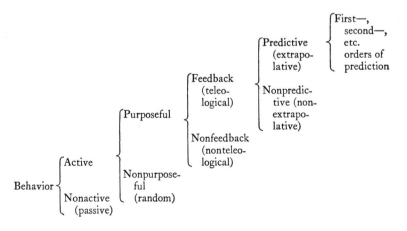

It is apparent that each of the dichotomies established singles out arbitrarily one feature, deemed interesting, leaving an amorphous remainder: the nonclass. It is also apparent that the criteria for the several dichotomies are heterogeneous. It is obvious, therefore, that many other lines of classification are available, which are independent of that developed above. Thus, behavior in general, or any of the groups in the table, could be divided into linear (that is, output proportional to input) and nonlinear. A division into continuous and discontinuous might be useful for many purposes. The several degrees of freedom which behavior may exhibit could also be employed as a basis of systematization.

The classification tabulated above was adopted for several reasons. It leads to the singling out of the class of predictive behavior, a class particularly interesting since it suggests the possibility of systematizing increasingly more complex tests of the behavior of organisms. It emphasizes the concepts of purpose and of teleology, concepts which, although rather discredited at present, are shown to be important. Finally, it reveals that a uniform behavioristic analysis is applicable to both machines and living organisms, regardless of the complexity of the behavior.

It has sometimes been stated that the designers of machines merely attempt to duplicate the performances of living organisms. This statement is uncritical. That the gross behavior of some machines should be similar to the reactions of organisms is not surprising. Animal behavior includes many varieties of all the possible modes of behavior and the machines devised so far have far from exhausted all those possible modes. There is, therefore, a considerable overlap of the two realms of behavior. Examples, however, are readily found of man-made machines with behavior that transcends human behavior. A machine with an electrical output is an instance; for men, unlike the electric fishes, are incapable of emitting electricity. Radio transmission is perhaps an even better instance, for no animal is known with the ability to generate short waves, even if so-called experiments on telepathy are considered seriously.

A further comparison of living organisms and machines leads to the following inferences. The methods of study for the two groups are at present similar. Whether they should always be the same may depend on whether or not there are one or more qualitatively distinct, unique characteristics present in one group and absent in the other. Such qualitative differences have not appeared so far.

The broad classes of behavior are the same in machines and in living organisms. Specific, narrow classes may be found exclusively in one or the other. Thus, no machine is available yet that can write a Sanskrit-Mandarin dictionary. Thus, also, no living organism is known that rolls on wheels—imagine what the result would have been if engineers had insisted on copying living organisms and had therefore put legs and feet in their locomotives, instead of wheels.

While the behavioristic analysis of machines and living organisms is largely uniform, their functional study reveals deep differences. Structurally, organisms are mainly colloidal, and include prominently protein molecules, large, complex and anisotropic; machines are chiefly metallic and include mainly simple molecules. From the standpoint of their energetics, machines usually exhibit relatively large differences of potential, which permit rapid mobilization of energy; in organisms the energy is more uniformly distributed; it is not very mobile. Thus, in electric machines conduction is mainly electronic, whereas in organisms electric changes are usually ionic.

Scope and flexibility are achieved in machines largely by temporal multiplication of effects; frequencies of one million per second or more are readily obtained and utilized. In organisms, spatial multiplication, rather than temporal, is the rule; the temporal achievements are poor—the fastest nerve fibers can only conduct about one thousand impulses per second; spatial multiplication is, on the other hand, abundant and admirable in its compactness. This difference is well illustrated by the comparison of a television receiver and the eye. The television receiver may be described as a single cone retina; the images are formed by scanning—that is, by orderly successive detection of the signal with a rate of about 20 million per second. Scanning is a process which seldom or never occurs in organisms, since it requires fast frequencies for effective performance. The eye uses a spatial, rather than a temporal multiplier. Instead of the one cone of the television receiver a human eye has about 6.5 million cones and about 115 million rods.

If an engineer were to design a robot, roughly similar in behavior to an animal organism, he would not attempt at present to make it out of proteins and other colloids. He would probably build it out of metallic parts, some dielectrics, and many vacuum tubes. The movements of the robot could readily be much faster and more powerful than those of the original organism. Learning and memory, however, would be quite rudimentary. In future years, as the knowledge of colloids and proteins increases, future engineers may attempt the design of robots not only with a behavior, but also with a structure similar to that of a mammal. The ultimate model of a cat is of course another cat, whether it be born of still another cat or synthesized in a laboratory.

In classifying behavior the term "teleology" was used as synonymous with "purpose controlled by feedback." Teleology has been interpreted in the past to imply purpose, and the vague concept of a "final cause" has been often added. This concept of final causes has led to the opposition of teleology to determinism. A discussion of causality, determinism, and final causes is beyond the scope of this essay. It may be pointed out, however, that purposefulness, as defined here, is quite independent of causality, initial or final. Teleology has been discredited chiefly because it was defined to imply a cause subsequent in time to a given effect. When this aspect of teleology was dismissed, however, the associated recognition of the importance of purpose was also unfortunately discarded. Since we consider purposefulness a concept necessary for the understanding of certain modes of behavior, we suggest that a teleological study is useful if it avoids problems of causality and concerns itself merely with an investigation of purpose.

We have restricted the connotation of teleological behavior by applying this designation only to purposeful reactions which are controlled by the error of the reaction—that is, by the difference between the state of the behaving object at any time and the final state interpreted as the purpose. Teleological behavior thus becomes synonymous with behavior controlled by negative feedback, and gains therefore in precision by a sufficiently restricted connotation.

According to this limited definition, teleology is not opposed to determinism, but to nonteleology. Both teleological and nonteleological systems are deterministic when the behavior considered belongs to the realm where determinism applies. The concept of teleology shares only one thing with the concept of causality: a time axis. But causality implies a one-way, relatively irreversible functional relationship, whereas teleology is concerned with behavior, not with functional relationships.

COMMENTS ON
A MECHANISTIC CONCEPTION
OF PURPOSEFULNESS

RICHARD TAYLOR

In a highly original and provocative essay entitled "Behavior, Purpose, and Teleology", published a few years ago,[1] Professors Arturo Rosenblueth, Norbert Wiener and Julian Bigelow attempt to indicate the scientific importance and usefulness of the concepts of purpose and teleology. Since this essay appeared the suggestions it contains seem to have acquired a significance which was not wholly apparent at that time. This is due primarily to the fact that a somewhat novel and, it appears to some, revolutionary approach to certain problems has arisen in the sciences, an approach which is more or less loosely referred to as "cybernetics," and among whose outstanding spokesmen are to be found the very authors of this essay—particularly Professor Wiener, whose recently published *Cybernetics*[2] has been claiming the attention of an increasing number of scientists and nonscientists alike. In his book, it may

"*Comments on a Mechanistic Conception of Purposefulness*," Philosophy of Science, *Vol. XVII* (1950), *pp. 310-317. Copyright* © *1950. The Williams &* Wilkins Co., Baltimore 2, Md., U.S.A.

[1] *Philosophy of Science,* Vol. X, 18-24 (1943). [See above, pp. 9–16]

[2] New York: John Wiley & Sons, Inc., 1948.

be noted, Professor Wiener, in tracing the development of cybernetics over the past few years, gives a good indication of the importance he attaches to the earlier essay. He writes, with reference to it: "The three of us [Rosenblueth, Wiener and Bigelow] felt that this new point of view merited a paper, which we wrote up and published. Dr. Rosenblueth and I foresaw that the paper could only be a statement of program for a large body of experimental work, and we decided that if we could ever bring our plan for an interscientific institute to fruition, this topic would furnish an almost ideal center for our activity." It would seem, then, that an examination of the contents of this essay should not be without interest at this time.

My objective in this paper will be to elicit what appears to be a gross confusion underlying these authors' main contention. This contention is that the notions of purpose and teleology, "although rather discredited at present," are in fact not only useful and important, but unavoidable and necessary for the interpretation of certain kinds of behavior, both animate and inanimate. I shall maintain, on the contrary, that these concepts, as they are defined and illustrated by these authors, cannot possibly serve the ends for which they are invoked. This conclusion will be indicated, I believe, if it can be shown (1) that purposive behavior, as they describe it, is indistinguishable from any other kind of active behavior, and (2) that the term "purpose," as thus used, bears no similarity whatever to the meaning which is ordinarily attached to it. This second point might seem to be largely a verbal matter, and indeed it is; but it would be a mistake to conclude from this that it is therefore of slight significance.

The concept of purposiveness is applied by these authors only to certain kinds of *active* behavior, that is to say, to that kind of behavior "in which the object is the source of the output energy involved in a given specific reaction." And the term "behavior" itself is taken to mean "any change of an entity with respect to its surroundings," [3] or, "any modification of an object, detectable externally." Thus, examples of active behavior would be, as I understand the definition, such things as a clock which is running, an automobile in operation, an exploding bomb, as well as the active behavior of living organisms generally. Passive behavior, on the other hand, that is, behavior in which "the object is not a source of energy," and in which "all the energy in the output can be traced to the immediate input," would be exemplified by such things as a falling stone, melting ice, and a revolving water wheel. The terms "active" and "passive" are themselves quite unambiguous, and serve to convey, I believe, the distinction intended. But it needs particularly to be noted at this point that active behavior is taken to characterize certain inanimate objects, no less than living ones.

[3] On this definition, it may be noted, a perfectly static object surrounded by others in motion exhibits "behavior."

With these distinctions in mind, we can consider now the discussion of purposefulness itself. The authors define purposeful and nonpurposeful behavior in these words: "The term 'purposeful' is meant to denote that the act or behavior may be interpreted as directed to the attainment of a goal—that is, to a final condition in which the behaving object reaches a definite correlation in time or in space with respect to another object or event. Purposeless behavior, then, is that which is not interpreted as directed to a goal."

Now the writers concede that the words, "may be interpreted," are vague, but insist that "the recognition that behavior may sometimes be purposeful is unavoidable and useful." I do not see that the expression, "may be interpreted," is really vague; the words themselves seem to have reasonably precise meanings, and I think there is little danger of their being mistaken. I think what the writers probably have in mind is that the definition itself is rather *general*—and in this, I should certainly concur. Indeed, the definition is so broad that it not only fails to distinguish, even in some general way, the feature which it is intended to describe, but makes any behavior whatever, whether active *or* passive, a case of purposiveness. One or two examples will show this to be the case.

Imagine, for instance, a clock which runs properly for many years, and then breaks down at twelve o'clock, New Year's Eve—such behavior admirably fits every requirement of purposiveness. Or again, consider a more humble example, such as a stone which falls from a rooftop, and kills a passer-by; or, more simply still, one that just makes a dent in the ground. Now such behavior not only *may* be interpreted as that in which the behaving object "reaches a definite correlation in time or in space with respect to another object or event," but such an interpretation is precisely the one which constitutes a simple and, as far as it goes, accurate description of just what has taken place. It seems hardly necessary to multiply examples here, for a very little reflection will show that any instance of behavior one might choose will necessarily be a case of "purposefulness," whether one considers active or passive behavior. And the reason for this is very apparent: it is simply that any behavior culminates, at whatever point we choose to call its culmination, in a definite correlation in time or space between the behaving object and other objects or events.[4]

---

[4] The word "correlation" is not defined by these writers, and in fact they use it only once. I therefore assume it to have no special or technical meaning in their usage. Ordinarily, to say of two objects or events that they are correlated, is simply to say that they stand in some reciprocal or mutual relationship, that is, that they are co-related. The word is also used more precisely to indicate a constant relationship between kinds of objects or events, or to indicate that one is a universal accompaniment of the other, as when we speak of mental

Of course the definition specifies that purposeful behavior is that active behavior which may be interpreted as being *directed* toward such a goal. But this, so far as I can discern, can only mean either (a) that such behavior is directed by some purposeful being *other* than the behaving object itself—by a human being, for example; or (b) that the behaving object directs *itself* toward some correlation. Now the first meaning is clearly not what the authors intend, for in that case the purposiveness would reside, not in the object itself, but in the being who directs it; a hammer does not itself become purposeful by being used *for* the purpose of driving nails. But if we consider the second meaning, which is the only other possible one, innumerable difficulties arise. In the first place, it presupposes the as yet unjustified assumption that some mechanisms, other than living organisms, *are* "intrinsically purposeful," in the distinctive sense of directing themselves toward the attainment of "goals." But even if this assumption were granted, then it is at once clear that *any* correlation in time or space between the behaving object and other objects or events can be taken as precisely the one toward which the supposedly purposeful object "directs" itself. For it is at all times in some such state of correlation, and so long as we leave distinctively human purposes out of account, as these authors try rigorously to do, then there is no conceivable way of selecting *some* particular reciprocal relationship between the object and some state of affairs as being the "goal" toward which that object was directing itself. Of course it might be suggested that we select as the goal of the object some *final* correlation; indeed, this seems to be exactly what the authors have in mind, in reiterating the expression "final condition." But this is of little help, because (a) unless the behaving object is destroyed, there *is* no such final condition: so long as it exists, it exists in a state of reciprocal relationship with other objects and events; and (b) such a criterion is wholly arbitrary. It obliges us to assert that whenever a supposedly purposeful mechanism culminates in such a "final condition" (however this "culmination" might be determined), then that final condition is, *ipso facto,* the very "goal" toward which it was directing itself. So if the behavior of an organism, say, culminates in some such final condition as death, then we shall be required to conclude that precisely this was, by definition, its purpose, that is, the "goal" toward which it directed itself. And this seems palpably incorrect; it would render such an expression as "accidental death" quite meaningless, for example.

Clearly, then, we cannot expect much light from such descriptions as

---

states being correlated with brain processes, or of the hands of a clock being correlated with each other, and so on. The more general meaning is what the authors seem to have in mind in their definition, although the more precise one would not alter their argument.

these; they appear arbitrary, and so general as to make purposiveness a ubiquitous phenomenon. Let us turn now, then, to the actual examples which the writers submit of both purposeful and nonpurposeful behavior, to see whether these will serve any better to elicit the distinction intended.

It is a mistake, they contend, to regard all machines as purposeful, and in this they are doubtless correct; it seems to be a mistake which none but the overly superstitious would be likely to make, however. As examples of mechanical devices which are *not* purposeful, they suggest a roulette wheel, a clock, and a gun. A roulette, it is pointed out, is "designed precisely for purposelessness." And a clock, although it is designed to serve a purpose, in not in itself purposeful—because there is, again, no "final condition" toward which it "strives." The same consideration applies to the example of a gun; it can, to be sure, be used for a purpose, but purposiveness itself "is not intrinsic to the performance of the gun," because it can also be shot at random.

As contrasted with these mechanisms, on the other hand, the authors cite the example of a torpedo containing a target-seeking device, as being an instance of a machine which is "intrinsically purposeful." Indeed, they single out an entire class of mechanical devices as possessing intrinsic purposiveness, namely, "servomechanisms," or machines which are controlled by negative feedback;[5] The term "servomechanisms," they note "has been coined precisely to designate machines with intrinsic purposeful behavior." Those who are acquainted with Professor Wiener's recent book[6] are aware of the importance he and his colleagues attach to these mechanisms. Before examining the discussion of these, however, a few remarks suggest themselves concerning the examples already referred to.

In the first place, it is difficult to see, from the descriptions given, in what sense roulettes, clocks, and guns are "purposeless," as contrasted with other mechanisms in which purposefulness is "intrinsic." A gun, it is pointed out, may be used for a purpose, but it can also be shot at random: therefore, "the attainment of a goal is not intrinsic to the performance of the gun." It would seem, however, that whether the gun is "used for a deliberate purpose" (for example, shooting a duck), or simply shot at random, in either case it serves a purpose—if only the

---

[5] The expression "negative feedback" is a technical one of physics and engineering. The authors point out that they are using it "to signify that the behavior of an object is controlled by the margin of error at which the object stands at a given time with reference to a relatively specific goal," (p. 11). The same idea could be expressed by saying that an object is controlled by *negative* feedback when the effects of its behavior in turn act indirectly upon the object itself to *oppose* whatever it is doing (cf. *Cybernetics,* p. 115).

[6] *Op. cit.*

amusement of the gunner. Moreover, even target-seeking missiles, which are classed as "intrinsically purposeful," *can* be used for random shooting, or even left to rust away in an ammunition dump; why does this not indicate a parallel conclusion in their case? Apparently the authors are utilizing here an unnamed criterion of purposiveness.

The remarks concerning the behavior of clocks are similarly puzzling. A clock is denied the attribute of "intrinsic" purposefulness because "there is no specific final condition toward which the movement of the clock strives." But if mechanical devices are once granted the power of "striving" toward some goal or "final condition," then how are we to know that the final condition which a clock ultimately attains—say, breakdown, at a particular time and place—was not the very one toward which it was "striving"? The difficulty in such a supposition is no greater than in the case of target-seeking missiles, however great it may be in either case.

Finally, a roulette wheel is said to be "designed precisely for purposelessness," and by this the authors apparently have in mind that this device is designed in a manner such that it will not, in the long run, turn up any specific number, or order of numbers, more frequently than any other. Such, at any rate, is the distinguishing characteristic of an ideal roulette. How, then, should one describe a number wheel which has a weight affixed to its circumference, in a way so as to determine the wheel always to stop on the number six? Such a mechanism satisfies perfectly every condition of intrinsic purposefulness which the writers set down; unlike the clock, for example, there *is* here a "specific final condition toward which the movement of the [wheel] strives"—provided, again, that "striving" may without incongruity be attributed to mechanical devices.

I question whether anyone would undertake to defend such a conclusion as this, first, because it seems *prima facie* bizarre to maintain that a wheel becomes a purposeful object by the mere addition to it of a weight, and secondly, because if it were maintained that such behavior as this is purposive, then it would be difficult to find an instance of behavior which is not. Yet, I submit, this conclusion is absolutely forced by the descriptions and criteria which the authors adduce. Now I should suppose that the only relevant distinction to be drawn between an honest roulette and a weighted one is that in the case of the second we can usually predict its "final condition," whereas in the case of the first we cannot. But the reason for this is not that the one is purposeless while the other is not, but rather that we know, and can measure, the causal factors involved in the behavior of the loaded wheel, whereas we do not have such knowledge with respect to the other. If, on the other hand, we *did* know all of the causal factors (force, mass, friction, and so forth) involved in the behavior of an honest roulette, then we *could,* within the limits of accuracy of our measuring instruments, predict its final condition, that is, the number on which it will stop; at least, this ability is universally taken for granted in the sciences, so long as we are dealing with such relatively macroscopic objects as wheels and the like. In what sense, then, is a roulette wheel a purposeless machine? So far as I can discern, the distinction to be made, as regards purposiveness, is simply this, and this only: If a purposive *being,* that is, a man, spins a roulette with the *purpose* of turning up a specific number, then he will be less likely to succeed if he uses an honest wheel, than if he uses one which is weighted properly; and the only reason for this is, again, that his knowledge of the causal factors involved in the behavior of the first wheel is insufficient to enable him to predict. And if this is a correct description, then, I submit, neither purposefulness nor purposelessness is appropriately attributable to the wheel, of whichever kind, but only to the being who uses it *for* a purpose.

The objective of the examples we have been considering was to elicit the distinction between purposeful and purposeless behavior—a distinction which the writers believe, correctly, is not made sufficiently clear by their definition. And the distinction which is apparently intended is simply this: that although such objects as roulette wheels, clocks, and guns can be made to *serve* a purpose, they do not have any purposes of their own; while a target-seeking missile, on the other hand, not only serves a purpose, but *does* have a purposiveness of its own; it is, in the words of the authors, an "intrinsically purposeful" object. At least, so far as the notion of "purpose" is concerned, this is the only distinction I can discern between machines which only serve a purpose, on the one hand, and those which are "intrinsically purposeful," on the other. As soon, however, as this distinction is made clear and precise, instead of simply hovering vaguely in the background, then, I believe, its dubious status becomes quite apparent.

Let us consider, finally, that class of machines which are distinguished by the possession of "intrinsic purposeful behavior," namely, servomechanisms. The term "servomechanisms" is used to denote such objects as thermostats, target-seeking missiles, ship steering devices, radar-controlled guns, and so on, the distinguishing characteristic of which is that the behavior of all such objects is controlled by negative feedback. That is to say, such a mechanism is so designed that the *effects* of its behavior themselves enter as causal factors *on* its behavior, the objective being to have a device that will maintain itself in a certain desired correlation with other objects or events, which also operate upon it as causal factors. This is doubtless an over-simple description, but I think it will do for our purposes. Thus, a thermostat controls, and is in turn controlled by, temperature; a target-seeking missile is directed at, and is in turn directed by, its target, and so on. In the case of all such mechanisms, then, the objects or events which they operate upon, in turn operate upon them, in such a manner as to maintain a constant reciprocal relationship. The governor of a steam engine was, I believe, one of the earliest of such man-made devices.

Professor Wiener and his colleagues regard these mechanisms as exhibiting a kind of purposiveness *par excellence,* namely, *teleological* purposefulness;[7] they maintain, in fact, that the concepts of purpose and teleology are not only useful, but necessary for the understanding of this class of machines. It seems significant to note, however, that what is here called "teleological purposeful behavior" is by no means limited to higher organisms and servomechanisms, but is exhibited as well by some of the most ordinary objects of our daily experience—a fact which these authors entirely neglect to point out. The leaves of many green plants, for example, follow the course of the sun, and thus exhibit a behavior pattern which is precisely the same, so far as teleology is concerned, as that of a machine which is designed to impinge upon a moving, luminous object—a servomechanism which is cited by the writers as clearly exemplifying teleological behavior. Again, consider the needle of an ordinary magnetic compass. If it is diverted from its alignment with the magnetic forces of its locus, it vacillates momentarily, and finally resumes its former correlation. The behavior of the compass thus fits precisely the description of a "purposeful reaction," as being that which is exhibited by an object whose behavior "is controlled by the margin of error at which the object stands at a given time with reference to a relatively specific goal," assuming that we can designate its final correlation with the magnetic forces as its "goal." Other examples, such as the behavior of a pendulum, or of a vibrating cord, come readily to mind; and if servomechanisms differ in any way, other than that of mere mechanical complexity, from such everyday phenomena as these, then the writers have at any rate failed to give any hint as to what this difference might be. The behavior of servomechanisms does, to be sure, satisfy perfectly the criteria of purposiveness which the authors adduce, but the behavior of these other objects seems to satisfy them equally well.

I should maintain, therefore, that the notions of purpose and teleology are not only useless for the understanding of this sort of mechanical behavior, but are wholly incongruous as thus applied; and this conclusion follows, I believe, from the fact that such behavior is describable in terms of, and only in terms of, the the same fundamental categories as are employed for the description of any other physical process.

---

[7] This expression may appear as a redundancy, but the authors qualify as "teleological" only those purposeful objects which are controlled by negative feedback.

A single example should make this last point clear. Consider the illustration used by the authors, namely, that of a torpedo with a target-seeking mechanism. Now if such a machine is so designed as to be guided by, say, sound waves proceeding from the ship's engines or propellers, then its behavior is describable, in general, as follows. The sound waves emanating from the target act causally upon the sonic mechanism of the torpedo, and the behavior of this device in turn acts (through intermediary devices) as a cause upon the steering mechanism of the missile. Accordingly, if the torpedo is diverted from its course, the resulting change in the sound waves, relative to the sonic device, suffices to reorient the torpedo, that is, causes it to resume its course, relative to the target. Similarly, if the target itself moves, the correlation between sound waves and missile is likewise upset, and this, again, suffices to alter the course of the torpedo, relative to the target, through the complex nexus of causes and effects obtaining between the sound waves and the torpedo's rudders and vanes. Of course an accurate description of this process is much less simple than this, but, I submit, such further description consists only in the addition of details to this general picture. And one point to note here is that the torpedo is guided, *not* by the target itself, but by the sound waves impinging upon the sonic mechanism; it does not literally "seek" the target, for its behavior would be the same even if no target were there, provided only that sound waves, or certain other immediate causes, obtained. The expression "target-seeking missile" is, in fact, metaphorical.

Is there, then, any room in such a description for the notion of *intrinsic* purposefulness on the part of the torpedo? I think not; and to illustrate this, we need only to alter the example in one respect. Let us suppose that the missile, instead of being governed by sound waves, is propelled along a cable, attached to the target. Now the behavior of this missile is precisely analogous to the first, the only relevant difference being that whereas the first was guided by sound waves between itself and the target, this one is guided by the much simpler means of a cable. If this second torpedo is diverted from its path, the change in its alignment, relative to the cable, suffices to reorient it; and the same is true if the target itself moves. In short, the analogy seems complete, the *only* difference being in the degree of mechanical complexity—and I doubt whether anyone would contend that complexity by itself is a criterion of a purposive object. Accordingly, if the first missile is to be characterized as "intrinsically purposeful," then we are obliged to conclude that the second one must be similarly described. But from this concession it would follow that a vast number of other machines become "intrinsically purposeful" objects, even though no one has ever suspected them of being such; trains, for example, or elevators, and in fact almost any machine one might choose.

My conclusion with respect to servomechanisms is, therefore, the same as before; namely, that Professors Rosenblueth, Wiener, and Bigelow (a) utilize criteria which render purposeful behavior a ubiquitous phenomenon, and (b) thereby endow the word "purpose" with a meaning having no similarity to any meaning it has customarily been taken to possess. Of course it might be claimed that one is entitled to assign to his terms any meaning he chooses, and in a sense this is true; it must be added, however, that if this is what these writers have done, then their discussion sacrifices any interest and significance which it may have been intended to have. For it is exactly as if one were to announce the discovery that $2 + 3 = 6$, only to add later that the term "+" is taken by him to have the meaning which has traditionally been assigned to the symbol "×". His claim would be entirely correct, but scarcely significant.

CAUSAL AND TELEOLOGICAL EXPLANATION

RICHARD BEVAN BRAITHWAITE

Any proper answer to a "Why?" question may be said to be an explanation of a sort. So the different kinds of explanation can best be appreciated by considering the different sorts of answers that are appropriate to the same or to different "Why?" questions.

What is demanded in a "Why?" question is intellectual satisfaction of one kind or another, and this can be provided, partially or completely, in different ways. Frequently the questioner does not know beforehand what sort of answer will satisfy him. And what gives partial or complete intellectual satisfaction to one person may give none whatever to a person at a different stage of intellectual development. A small child, for example, is frequently satisfied by a confident reassertion of the fact about which he has asked the "Why?" question. This is not foolishness on his part. The child is prepared to accept the fact without question on authority; what he is doubtful about is whether the authority is good enough, and a confident reassertion by the person to whom he has asked the "Why?" question may serve to

From Scientific Explanation *by R. B. Braithwaite, by permission of the Cambridge University Press.*

strengthen the authority sufficiently for him to feel complete satisfaction in accepting it.

When an adult wishes for satisfaction of this purely confirmatory sort, he phrases his question in the form "Is it really the case that . . .?", reserving his "Why?" questions for cases in which he requires for satisfaction something more than a repetition of the "Why?" sentence with the omission of the "Why." What he requires is explanation in the proper sense of the proffering of an explicans-proposition as an explanation of the explicandum-fact about which he has asked the "Why?" question, the explicans being required to be different from the explicandum.

Different sorts of explicanda call for different sorts of explanation— or, at least, for different sorts of first-stage explanations. The primary explicanda for science are particular empirical facts; and first-stage explanations of these are of two types. When an adult asks "Why f?" of a particular matter of fact f, he is usually wanting either a *causal explanation* expressed by the sentence "Because of g" or a *teleological explanation* expressed by the sentence "In order that g." Each of these types of explanation will involve an explicit or implicit reference to scientific laws; a "Why?" question asked of a scientific law (and this may well be a second-stage "Why?" question asked of a particular matter of fact) will be a request, not for a cause or for a teleological goal, but for a reason for the scientific law being what it is. This chapter will be devoted to the first-stage explanation of particular empirical facts, a discussion of the explanation of scientific laws themselves being postponed until the next chapter.

CAUSAL EXPLANATION

. . . When a person asks for a cause of a particular event (for example, the fall of this picture to the floor at noon yesterday), what he is requesting is the specification of a preceding or simultaneous event which, in conjunction with certain unspecified cause factors of the nature of permanent conditions, is nomically sufficient to determine the occurrence of the event to be explained (the explicandum-event) in accordance with a causal law, in one of the customary senses of "causal law." [1] The "Why?" question is not expected to be answered

---

[1] By saying that an event having the property B is *nomically determined* by an event having the property A, in conjunction with events having property A_1, having property A_2, and so forth, no more is meant than that the generalization ≪Every conjunction of an event having A with events having A_1, A_2, and so forth, is associated with an event having B≫ is a true generalization. Use of the language of nomic determination does not, therefore, presuppose any non-Humean analysis either of nomic or of causal statements.

by detailing all the events which together make up a total cause, that is, a set of events which collectively determine the explicandum-event; all that is usually expected is the part-cause which is of most interest to the questioner—which presumably is that of which he is ignorant. One sense of giving a *complete* explanation would be that of specifying a total cause; in this sense, as indeed in most senses of complete explanation, a "complete explanation" will not be unique, since (in almost all senses of "cause") the same event can perfectly well have many different total causes.

There are various complications about causal explanations considered as answers to "Why?" questions which need not detain us long. The formal explanation just given is that in which the questioner is taken to be asking for a *sufficient condition* for the explicandum-event, or for part of a sufficient condition, the other part being supposed to be already known. The explicans in such an explanation is an event the occurrence of which possessing a certain property, in conjunction with other events with suitable properties, nomically determines the occurrence of the explicandum-event with a certain property. So the existence of the explicans-event ensures the existence of the explicandum-event. But the "Why?" question is sometimes a request for a *necessary condition* for the explicandum-event; it then asks for the specification of an event which is such that, had it not occurred, the explicandum-event would also not have occurred. In this case it is the explicans-event which is nomically determined by the explicandum-event instead of the other way around. And frequently the "Why?" question requires as answer the specification of an event which is both one of a set of events which together form a sufficient condition and one which in the presence of the rest of the set of events is a necessary condition for the occurrence of the explicandum-event.

There is one type of causal explanation which, rightly or wrongly, gives great intellectual satisfaction to those who have been educated in the contemporary natural sciences—namely, causal explanations making use of causal laws which are causal according to [a] criterion III'.[2] Here an event to be acceptable as explicans must be the first member of a *causal chain* of events ending with the explicandum, a spatio-temporally continuous chain of events being said to form a causal chain if every event in the chain nomically determines its neighbors in the chain in such a way that the causal law relating the explicans-event with the explicandum-event is a consequence within a true deductive system of higher-level laws which relate only spatio-temporally continuous events. The intellectual satisfaction provided by an explanation which cites a "causal ancestor" is due partly to the great success of such

---

[2] This criterion was stated by Braithwaite in a previous chapter. Its substance is given in the remarks immediately following. Ed.

explanations in the physical sciences, but partly also to the fact that, if the deductive system whose highest-level hypotheses relate spatio-temporally continuous events is unrefuted by the evidence, there will be a great deal of evidence which supports it. For an unlimited number of lower-level hypotheses about causal ancestries will be deducible from the highest-level hypotheses, and the falsity of some, at least, of these would be expected to leap to the eye if the highest-level hypotheses were false.

At the other extreme there is a type of explanation based upon generalizations which have been established by direct induction without any indirect hypothetico-deductive support. These generalizations, therefore, do not satisfy the conditions for being entitled "natural laws," and consequently cannot be classed as causal laws. . . . So these explanations cannot be called causal explanations. Nevertheless they can give some intellectual satisfaction, for they give information on one point about which the questioner may be ignorant. Molière was right in laughing at the doctors who offered the *virtus dormitiva* of opium as the answer to the question as to why opium produced sleep.[3] But it would not be foolish to answer the question as to why a particular specimen of powder produced sleep by replying that it was because that powder was opium, and that opium had the property of producing sleep. For this would inform a questioner who did not know it already that the powder produced sleep, not by virtue of its color, degree of powderedness, and so forth, but by virtue of its chemical composition. Similarly, when a child asks "Why is this bird white?", the reply "Because it is a swan, and all English swans are white" tells him that the whiteness is not a peculiarity of this particular bird, and thus shows the particular case to be an instance of a general proposition.

TELEOLOGICAL EXPLANATION

We must now turn to a type of explanation which has so far not been discussed—a type which has given rise to a great deal of discussion among philosophers and philosophically minded biologists, because it has been thought to raise peculiar scientific and philosophical difficulties. This type of explanation is that in which the "Why?" question about a particular event or activity is answered by specifying a goal or end towards the attainment of which the event or activity is a means. Such explanations will be called "teleological explanations."[4] If I am asked why I am staying in Cambridge all through August, I should reply

---

[3] In the third ballet scene of *Le Malade Imaginaire*.

[4] The remainder of this chapter follows, with some alterations and additions, the text of my 1946 Presidential Address to the Aristotelian Society (*Proceedings of the Aristotelian Society*, n.s., Vol. XLVII (1946-7), i ff.).

"In order to finish writing my book"; to reply thus would be to give a teleological explanation. If I am asked why my cat paws at the door on a particular occasion, I might well reply "In order that I should open the door for it"—another teleological explanation. If an ornithologist is asked why a cuckoo lays its egg in the nest of another bird, and replies "So that the other bird may hatch out and nurture its young," or if a physiologist is asked why the heart beats, and replies "To circulate the blood round the body" or (in more detail) "To convey oxygen from the lungs to the tissues and carbon dioxide from the tissues to the lungs" or (in terms of an ultimate biological end) "In order that the body may continue to live," he will be giving in each case a teleological explanation of the action in terms of the goal or end of the action. The explanation consists in stating a goal to be attained: it describes the action as one directed towards a certain goal—as a "goal-directed activity" (to use E. S. Russell's convenient phrase[5]), the word "directed" being used (as it will here be used) to imply a direction but not to imply a director.

If we take an explanation (as we are doing) to be any answer to a "Why?" question which in any way answers the question, and thereby gives some degree of intellectual satisfaction to the questioner, there can be no doubt that teleological answers of the sort of which I have given examples are genuine explanations. The fact that they all may give rise to further questions does not imply that they are not perfectly proper answers to the questions asked. My answer as to why I am staying in Cambridge all through August would almost certainly not lead to a further question, unless my friend wished to start a philosophical discussion as to the correct analysis of the motives of rational action. My answer as to why my cat paws the door might lead to the further question as to why the cat (to use common-sense language) "wants to be let out," to which another teleological answer would be appropriate, or to the question as to how the cat has learned to paw the door to show that he wants to be let out, which would lead to a description, which might or might not be in teleological terms, of the processes of learning in cats. But all these would be regarded as further and different questions; the first simple teleological answer would be taken as what the questioner was asking for, and if it did not give him adequate intellectual satisfaction, he would expect not to repeat the question but to ask another.

But, having insisted that teleological explanations are perfectly good first-stage explanations, we have to admit that they have one feature which distinguishes them from causal explanations, and that this feature has proved very puzzling to philosophers, whether concerned with

---

[5] *The Directiveness of Organic Activities* (London: University of Cambridge Press, 1945).

philosophical psychology or with the philosophy of biology. In a causal explanation the explicandum is explained in terms of a cause which either precedes or is simultaneous with it; in a teleological explanation the explicandum is explained as being causally related either to a particular goal in the future or to a biological end which is as much future as present or past. It is the reference in teleological explanations to states of affairs in the future, and often in the comparatively distant future, which has been a philosophical problem ever since Aristotle introduced the notion of "final cause"; the controversy as to the legitimacy of explanations in terms of final causes rages continually among philosophers of biology and, to a less extent, among working biologists.

Now there is one type of teleological explanation in which the reference to the future presents no difficulty, namely, explanations of an intentional human action in terms of a goal to the attainment of which the action is a means. For my teleological answer to the question as to why I am staying in Cambridge all through August—that I am doing so in order to finish writing my book—would be regarded by my questioner as equivalent to an answer that I am doing so because I intend to finish writing my book, my staying in Cambridge being a means to fulfill that intention; and this answer would have been an explanation of the causal sort with my intention as cause preceding my stay in Cambridge as effect. [6] Teleological explanations of intentional goal-directed activities are always understood as reducible to causal explanations with intentions as causes; to use the Aristotelian terms, the idea of the "final cause" functions as "efficient cause"; the goal-directed behavior is explained as goal-intended behavior.

This is not to say that there is no philosophical difficulty about intentional action; there is the problem—fundamental for philosophical psychology—as to the correct analysis of the intention to act in a certain way. But this is different from our problem as to how a future reference can occur in an explanation, unless indeed an extreme behavioristic analysis is adopted, according to which there is no conscious element in an intention, and goal-intended behavior is simply what we call goal-directed behavior in the higher animals. But for this extreme behaviorism psychology reduces to biology, and intentional action falls under biological goal-directed activity and the type of teleological ex-

---

[6] Jonathan Cohen has pointed out (*Proceedings of the Aristotelian Society,* n.s., Vol. LI (1950-1), 262 ff.) that such an explanation would differ from an ordinary causal explanation in that it is more difficult to specify the total cause of which the intention is only a part than it is to specify the total cause in an ordinary causal explanation. But this difference is only one of degree (as Cohen seems prepared to admit; *loc. cit.* p. 268 n.); and, however partial the intention may be as a factor in a total cause, it will not be later in time than the action which it is put forward to explain.

planation we meet in the sciences concerned with life in general and not especially with mind.

The difficulty about the future reference occurs then in all teleological explanations which are not reducible to explanations in terms of a conscious intention to attain the goal. Here one cannot obviously reduce the teleological answer, which explains a present event by means of a future event, to a nonteleological answer in terms of a present or past cause. It is teleological explanations which cannot obviously be so reduced which present the philosophical problem; and the rest of this chapter will be devoted to this type of teleological explanations and to the problems raised by them.

CURRENT ATTEMPTS TO ELIMINATE FINAL CAUSES

There are two ways of solving this problem which are fashionable today. Both are attempts to reduce all teleological explanations to causal explanations, and thus to eliminate the special puzzle presented by future reference; but the attempts are made in opposite directions.

The first way is to emphasize the similarity between teleological explanations of the type with which we are now concerned and the teleological explanations of intentional actions in which the future reference can be explained away, and to argue by analogy that in all cases the teleological explanation is reducible to one in which an intention, or something analogous to an intention, in the agent is the "efficient cause," so that goal-directed activity is always a sort of goal-intended activity. My cat's behavior in pawing at the closed door, it may be said, is sufficiently similar to a man's behavior in knocking at a locked door for it to be reasonable to infer that the cat, like the man, is acting as it does because of a conscious intention, or at least a conscious desire, to be let through the door. Similarly a neurotic's goal-directed behavior may be explained by his having an unconscious intention or desire; a bird's nest-building by its having an instinct to do so. When the goal-directed activity to be explained is that of a part of a whole organism, as in my example of the heart's beating, the analogue to the intention— the drive or conatus or nisus or urge—is usually posited not in the separate organ but in the organism as a whole—an urge towards self-preservation, for example. Sometimes the analogy is pressed so far that a purposiveness similar to that of voluntary action is assumed in all teleological behavior. William McDougall, for instance, after explaining that by "purposiveness" in human movements he means not only that "they are made for the sake of attaining their natural end" (that is, that they are teleological in my sense), but that "this end is more or less clearly anticipated or foreseen," goes on to speak of a "scale of degrees of purposiveness," at the lower end of which there is a "vague anticipation of the goal" which may also be ascribed to an animal's goal-directed behavior.[7]

Other writers (for example, E. S. Russell) would reject as unduly anthropomorphic the attribution of purposiveness to such activities, and would describe the efficient cause as a conatus or drive. But all writers who deal with the problem of teleological explanation in the first way agree in postulating something in the organism which is present whenever goal-directed behavior is taking place and which is to explain it in the ordinary causal way, and agree in supposing that this something cannot be analyzed purely in physicochemical terms.

The biological orthodoxy of today, however, would say that the postulation of this "something," not explicable in physicochemical terms, to account for teleological behavior was an assumption which was either methodologically vicious (if the "something" was supposed to have no properties other than that of being the cause of the goal-directed behavior) or metaphysical and nonempirical (if it was supposed to have additional properties such as McDougall's purposiveness). And orthodox biologists would go on to say that satisfactory explanations had been given of many goal-directed activities in physicochemical terms, and that as the new sciences of biochemistry and biophysics advance, there is less and less reason to suppose that there will be any teleological action (or at any rate any teleological action in which consciousness is not involved) that will not be explicable by means of the concepts and laws of chemistry and physics alone.

This attitude is equivalent to an attempt to solve the problem of teleological explanations in a second way, by reducing them to physicochemical explanations of the ordinary causal sort. It is admitted that biochemistry and biophysics at the moment cannot effect this reduction in the great majority of cases, but it is expected that some day they will be able to. Teleological explanations must be accepted as irreducible to causal explanations at present, but not as in principle irreducible. Thus the philosophical problem presented by the reference to the future in such explanations is a temporary problem only, to be solved by the progress of science. A teleological explanation is to be regarded as a very poor sort of explanation indeed, to be discarded as soon as the real, physicochemical causes have been discovered.

It seems to me that the orthodox biologists are right in rejecting the postulation of a conatus or drive which is nonphysical and *sui generis* in order to explain the goal-directed behavior which they meet in their biological studies, but wrong in minimizing the intellectual satisfaction to be derived from teleological explanations. I believe that we can go

---

[7] W. McDougall, *An Outline of Psychology* (London: Methuen, 1923), pp. 47 f.

on the orthodox assumption that every biological event is physicochemically determined, and yet find an important place in biology for such explanations. So what I propose to do is to try to give an account of the nature of teleological explanations which will resolve the philosophical difficulty about the apparent determination of the present by the future without either contravening the usual determination principles of science or reducing all biological laws to those of chemistry and physics.[8]

TELEOLOGICAL CAUSAL CHAINS

If we make the ordinary determination assumptions of physical science, the apparent determination of the explicandum by a future event in a teleological explanation is not direct, but works by means of a causal chain of events lying between the explicandum and the goal. Even in intentional action the intention does not directly produce the goal: it starts a chain of action whose final stage is attainment of the goal. In nonintentional goal-directed action the goal-directedness consists simply in the fact that the causal chain in the organism goes in the direction of the goal, unless one wishes to suppose that there is always an extra "something"—conatus or drive—involved in goal-directedness, an assumption which I do not wish to make. Thus the notion of causal chain is fundamental. Of course this notion is equally fundamental in the nonteleological explanations provided by the physical sciences, where the explaining cause is frequently given not as a preceding event continuous with the explicandum but as a preceding event connected with the explicandum by a causal chain. Let us approach our problem, therefore, by asking what (if any) is the peculiarity of the causal chains which are involved in teleological explanations.

Bertrand Russell, in his behavioristic account of desire, approached our problem in the same way as I am doing by asserting that the peculiarity of teleological causal chains of actions is that they form "behavior-cycles." But the only criterion he gave to enable us to pick out the behavior-cycles from other repeated series of events in the life of an animal was that the final stage in a behavior-cycle is "normally a condition of temporary quiescence."[9] He illustrated this by an animal falling

---

[8] Analyses of teleological explanations which have more or less resemblance to my analysis have been given by E. Rignano, *Mind,* n.s., Vol. XL (1931), 337; A. Rosenblueth, N. Wiener and J. Bigelow, *Philosophy of Science,* Vol. X (1943), 24 ("Teleological behavior becomes synonymous with behavior controlled by negative feedback"); L. von Bertalanffy, *British Journal for the Philosophy of Science,* Vol. I (1950), 157. The field of study called by Wiener "cybernetics" is largely concerned with "teleological mechanisms."

[9] *The Analysis of Mind* (New York: The Macmillan Company, 1921), p. 65.

asleep after it has eaten. But temporary quiescence is quite inadequate to serve as the *differentia* for which we are seeking. After a bomb has exploded, or a volcano ceased to erupt, a state of temporary quiescence is attained. Here no teleology is concerned in the causal chains. It seems impossible to find any characteristic of the final state by itself of a teleological causal chain which is general enough to cover all the goals of goal-directed actions and yet specific enough to differentiate such actions from other repeated cycles of behavior. It is necessary, I think, to look at the whole causal chain and not merely at its final state.

It seems to me that a distinguishing criterion can be found in one of the characteristics which biologists have emphasized in their descriptions of goal-directed behavior, namely persistence towards the goal under varying conditions. To quote E. S. Russell: "Coming to a definite end or terminus is not *per se* distinctive of directive activity, for inorganic processes also move towards a natural terminus. . . . What *is* distinctive is the active persistence of directive activity towards its goal, the use of alternative means towards the same end, the achievement of results in the face of difficulties." [10] Examples of the "plasticity" of goal-directed behavior will spring to every mind. To give one example only, Lashley's rats who had learned to obtain their food by running his maze were still able to traverse the maze without false turns in order to obtain food after their powers of motor coordination had been seriously reduced by cerebellar operations, so that they could no longer run but could only crawl or lunge.[11] Plasticity is not in general a property of one teleological causal chain alone: it is a property of the organism with respect to a certain goal, namely that the organism can attain the same goal under different circumstances by alternative forms of activity making use frequently of different causal chains. Let us try to elucidate the logical and epistemological significance of this plasticity, in order to see whether it will serve our purpose of preserving the importance of teleological explanations without introducing extraphysical causation.

Consider a chain of events in a system b. The system may be a physical system of more or less complexity (a pilotless plane or an electron) or it may be an organic system (a complete organism or a relatively isolable part of a complete organism, for example, the kidneys). Make the ordinary determination assumption that every event in the system is nomically determined by the whole previous state of the system together with the causally relevant factors in the system's environment or field (which will be called the "field-conditions"). Then the causal chain c of events in b throughout a period of time is nomically determined

---

[10] *The Directiveness of Organic Activities* (London: Cambridge University Press, 1945), p. 144.

[11] K. S. Lashley, *Brain Mechanisms and Intelligence* (Chicago: University of Chicago Press, 1929).

by the initial state e of the system together with the totality of field-conditions which affect the system with respect to the events in question during the period. Call this set of field-conditions f. Then, for a given system b with initial state e, c is a one-valued function of f; that is, for given b and e, the causal chain c is uniquely determined by f—the set of field-conditions.

Now consider the property which a causal chain in a system may possess of ending in an event of type Γ without containing any other event of this type. Call this property the Γ–goal-attaining property, and the class of all causal chains having this property the Γ–goal-attaining class γ. Every causal chain which is a member of γ contains one and only one event of type Γ, and contains this as its final event.

Define the variancy ϕ with respect to a given system b with given initial state e, and to a given type of goal Γ, as the class of those sets of field-conditions which are such that every causal chain in b starting with e and determined by one of these sets is Γ–goal-attaining. To express this more shortly with the symbols already used, the variancy ϕ is defined as the class of those f's which uniquely determine those c's which are members of γ. According to this definition, to say that a causal chain c in a system b starting from a state e ends (without having previously passed through) a state of type Γ is logically equivalent to saying that the set of field-conditions is a member of ϕ. The variancy is thus (to repeat the definition in a looser form) the range of circumstances under which the system attains the goal.

The variancy ϕ defined in relation to b, e and Γ may have no members, in which case there is no nomically possible chain in b starting from e and attaining a goal of type Γ. Or ϕ may have one member, in which case there is exactly one such chain which is nomically possible. Here the system starting from e has no plasticity; there is only one set of field-conditions which, together with e, is nomically sufficient for the attainment of a goal of type Γ.

The case in which we are interested, in which the system has plasticity, occurs when the variancy ϕ has more than one member, so that the occurrence of any one of alternative sets of field-conditions is, together with e, sufficient for the attainment of a goal of type Γ. It is important to notice that the variancy may have many members and yet there be only one nomically possible chain: it is because the size of the variancy may be greater than the number of possible causal chains that the notion of the variancy has been introduced. For it may be the case that there are various sets of field-conditions each of which, together with e, determines exactly the same causal chain. This might happen if the ultimate causal laws concerned are such that each of the events in the chain might be determined by two or more alternative field-conditions. But it more frequently happens when the events in the chain are taken as being events which attribute properties to the system as a whole, and when, although alternative field-conditions determine different part-events in the system or in parts of the system, these part-events are causally so connected that the whole event determined by them remains unchanged. For example, if the causal chain of events with which we are concerned is the chain of body temperatures throughout a period of time of one of the higher animals, a change in the relevant environmental conditions (for example, external temperature and available sources of food) will produce changes in the activities of the animal (both changes in its total behavior, for example, its feeding and migration habits, and changes in its parts, for example, its sweat glands), yet these changes will be such as to compensate for the changed environmental conditions so that the animal's body temperature does not vary. Another example would be the path of a pilotless plane, in which the machine is fitted with "feedback" devices so designed that the plane will maintain a straight course at the correct height to the desired goal irrespective of the weather conditions it may encounter.

But usually when the variancy has more than one member, there is more than one nomically possible chain in the system in question which attains the required goal. An animal can move to get its food in many ways, a great variety of physiological processes can be called into play to repair damaged tissue, a bird can adapt its nest-building to the kind of material available. Nevertheless the essential feature, as I see it, about plasticity of behavior is that the goal can be attained under a variety of circumstances, not that it can be attained by a variety of means. So it is the size of the variancy rather than the number of possible causal chains that is significant in analyzing teleological explanation.

Let us now take the standpoint of epistemological or inductive logic and consider what are the types of situation in which we reasonably infer that there will be a goal-attaining chain of events in a system. To predict that, starting from an initial state e of a system b, there will be a causal chain which will attain a goal of type Γ is, by the definition of variancy, equivalent to predicting that the set of field-conditions which will occur will be a member of the variancy ϕ. So the reasonableness of the prediction depends upon the reasonableness of believing that ϕ is large enough to contain every set of field-conditions that is at all likely to occur.[12] Call the class of these sets of field-conditions ψ. For simplicity's sake I shall for the moment assume that we know that any set of field-conditions that will occur will be contained in ψ; that is, that the system will not in fact encounter a very unlikely environment (for example, the next Ice Age starting suddenly tomorrow). Then the

---

[12] The phrase "at all likely to occur" can be interpreted in different ways; but their difference does not affect the argument.

reasonableness of the prediction that the system will attain the goal depends upon the reasonableness of believing that ψ is included in ϕ.

Now there are two ways in which we may have derived our knowledge of the variancy ϕ. We may have deduced ϕ from knowledge of the relevant causal laws, or we may have inferred it inductively from knowledge of the sets of field-conditions under which similar causal chains had attained their goals in the past. In the first case, that in which the members of ϕ have been obtained by deduction, there are two interesting subcases in which we take positive steps to secure that ψ—the class of the sets of field-conditions at all likely to occur—is included in the variancy ϕ. The first subcase is that in which ϕ is small, but we deliberately arrange that ψ shall be smaller still. This happens when scientific demonstrations are performed for students in a laboratory, when elaborate precautions are taken (for example, the experiment is done in a vacuum or distilled water is used) in order to eliminate unwanted relevant causal factors (air currents or chemical impurities) and thus to secure that every set of conditions that may occur will fall within the known variancy ϕ so that the demonstration will be a success. The second subcase is that in which ψ is large, but we deliberately arrange that ϕ shall be larger still. This happens when a machine is deliberately designed to work under a large variety of conditions. This object may be achieved by using suitable materials: a motor-car is built to stand up to a lot of rough and careless treatment. Or it may be achieved by incorporating in the machine special self-regulating devices to insure that the machine adjusts its method of working according to the conditions it encounters, as in the pilotless plane.

When our knowledge of the relevant variancy has been obtained by deduction from previous knowledge of the causal laws concerned, a teleological explanation of an event in terms of its goal-directedness is felt to be almost valueless.[13] For in this case, that the causal chain which will occur will lead to the goal—the "teleology" of the system—has been calculated from its "mechanism." To give a teleological answer to the "Why?" question would require forming (and suppressing) an ordinary causal answer, which would (if expressed) have given intellectual satisfaction to the questioner, in order to deduce from it a teleological answer. This would be an unprofitable, and indeed disingenuous, way of answering his question.

---

[13] In the case of a machine or of a laboratory demonstration a teleological explanation can of course be given of the action of a man in starting and controlling the machine or demonstration. Derivatively we can apply such a teleological explanation (as a "transferred epithet") to the working of the machine itself. But these explanations are all in terms of intentions as efficient causes, and so do not raise the special problem with which we are here concerned.

The situation is entirely different when our knowledge or reasonable belief about the variancy ϕ has not been derived from knowledge of the causal laws concerned. In this case our knowledge as to what sets of conditions make up the variancy has been obtained either directly by induction from previous experience of goal-attaining behavior that was similar to the behavior with which we are concerned, or indirectly by deduction from general teleological propositions which have themselves been established by induction from past experience. Neither of these ways makes use of laws about the mechanisms of the causal chains. The variancy ϕ is inferred—inductively inferred—from knowledge of classes similar to ψ; that is, from past observation of the conditions under which similar teleological behavior has taken place. For example, my knowledge of the conditions under which a swallow will migrate is derived from knowledge about past migrations of swallows and of other migrants, fortified perhaps by general teleological propositions which I accept about the external conditions for self-preservation or the survival of the species, themselves derived inductively from past experience.

It is when our knowledge of the relevant variancy has been obtained independently of any knowledge of the causal laws concerned that a teleological explanation is valuable. For in this case we are unable, through ignorance of the causal laws, to infer the future behavior of the system from our knowledge of the causal laws; but we are able to make such an inference from knowledge of how similar systems have behaved in the past.

It should be noted that in all cases of teleological explanation of a present event by a future event, whether reducible or irreducible, inductive inferences occur at two stages of the argument. One stage is in the inference of the variancy, whether this itself is obtained inductively, or whether it is obtained deductively from causal laws or teleological generalizations which have themselves been established inductively. The other inductive stage in the argument is the inference that the set of relevant conditions that will in fact occur in the future will fall within the variancy. Every teleological answer, however reasonable, may be mistaken in each of these two ways.

But in general irreducible teleological explanations are no less worthy of credence than ordinary causal explanations. A teleological explanation of a particular event is intellectually valuable if it cannot be deduced from known causal laws: other things being equal, it is the more valuable the wider the variancy of the conditions, and hence the greater the plasticity of the behavior concerned. It is because we are acquainted with systems—organisms and parts of organisms—which exhibit great plasticity that we make use of teleological explanations. Such an explanation may be regarded as merely another way of stating the fact of the plasticity of the goal-directed behavior. But to state this fact is to bring the explicandum under a general category; moreover it enables us to make reliable predictions as to how the system will behave in the future. It seems ridiculous to deny the title of explanation to a statement which performs both of the functions characteristic of scientific explanations—of enabling us to appreciate connections and to predict the future.

The analysis which has here been given of teleological explanation of nonintentional goal-directed activities supposes that the goal to which the activity is directed is later in time than the action (this indeed creates the philosophical problem) and makes great use of the notion of causal chain. It has been objected that this analysis will not cover the case of explanations of biological facts which are given in terms, not of a future goal, but of a biological end which is as much present as future; but that this case, as well as that in which the explanation is in terms of a future goal, will be covered by the more general notion of *functional explanation* in which the explanation is in terms of another part of a whole of which the explicandum is a part.[14] But the questions which seem to call for a more general functional explanation rather than for a causal-chain teleological explanation turn out on examination to be ambiguous questions. If a physiologist is asked why the heart beats, he may take this question as a request for an explanation of a particular fact, the beating of a particular heart on a particular occasion, in which case the explanation "In order to circulate the blood round the body" will also refer to the movement of the blood in a particular body on a particular occasion. But, on this interpretation, the particular movement of blood outside the heart due to a particular beating of the heart is an event whose beginning is later in time than the beginning of the event which is the heart's beating: the latter event is connected with the former event by a causal chain of events, and is a teleological explanation of it in terms of a future goal. But the physiologist may more naturally take the question, not to be a question about one particular heart on one particular occasion, but to be a question about all beatings

---

[14] Jonathan Cohen, *Proceedings of the Aristotelian Society,* n.s., Vol. LI (1950-1), 270, 292. Cohen holds that "a functional explanation asserts the explanandum to be [a] necessary condition (logically, causally, or in any other generally recognized way) of the explanans and thereby also of the persistence under varying circumstances of a whole of which both explanans and the explanandum are parts" (*loc. cit.* p. 292). But the beating of my heart is not a *necessary* condition for the circulation of my blood: it is only because my anatomy includes a heart but no other mechanism for circulating my blood that it is causally necessary that the heart should *beat* in order that the blood should circulate.

of all hearts (or of all human hearts, or of all mammalian hearts, or and so forth), in which case the question is a request for a teleological generalization of which the particular teleological explanation of the beating of one particular heart on one particular occasion would be an instance. In both cases, however, the explanation would be in terms of goal-directed activities with future goals. The peculiarity of a biological end is that it is a permanent goal; at all times during the life of the organism there are activities of the organism to be explained in terms of the biological end. My heart's beating at one moment is responsible for the circulation of my blood a short time afterwards; and my heart will have to *continue* beating for my blood to *continue* circulating. The teleological generalization of which the particular teleological explanation of the beating of my heart on a particular occasion is an instance will have instances at every moment of my life, unlike teleological laws concerning goals upon the attainment of which the animal sinks into a "temporary quiescence." [15]

TELEOLOGICAL LAWS

We have referred in several places to teleological generalizations. Just as particular causal explanations are instances of causal propositions, of more or less generality, so particular teleological explanations are instances of teleological generalizations of more or less generality; that is, they (if true) are instances of laws according to which an event of a certain sort in a system of a certain sort is nomically determined by a later event of a certain sort in the same system. Such a teleological law will be valuable as an explanation if it has not been deduced from nonteleological laws, and it will be the more valuable both intellectually and predictively the wider the range of the variancy associated with it.

The special philosophical difficulty about teleological, as contrasted with causal, explanations of particular events—namely, that in them the present appears to be determined by the future—does not arise in the case of teleological as contrasted with nonteleological laws, considered as laws of nature without regard to their applications to yield particular explanations. For many nonteleological laws of nature, for example, Newton's laws of mechanics, are symmetrical with respect to the earlier and later times occurring in the laws: they state that the present is determined by the future just as much as it is determined by

---

[15] The term "functional explanation" may sometimes also be used to cover a mere description of the *modus operandi* of an organ like the heart. This would correspond to J. H. Woodger's third sense of "function" (*Biological Principles* [New York: Harcourt, Brace & World, Inc., 1929], p. 327).

the past. Nor do teleological laws in general differ from nonteleological ones in having a time-interval between the two related events: many nonteleological laws are about what happens during a period of time taken as a whole, for example, the Law of Least Action. The difference between the two types of law seems to consist simply in the way in which the related variancy is discovered.

Here a comparison may be made with another type of law of a somewhat peculiar nature which occurs in psychology and in biology, and which shares with the teleological type the two characteristics that there is an interval of time between the determining and the determined event, and that the law holds under a wide variety of conditions which have been discovered inductively and not deductively. I refer to the laws governing what Bertrand Russell called "mnemic phenomena," laws which he called "mnemic laws." [16] The simplest example of such a law is that of memory recall, in which a present memory-image is determined (partially determined) by the occurrence in the rememberer of an experience of which the present memory-image is an image; but there are plenty of nonpsychological examples in biology. The Mendelian laws of heredity state that sometimes some of the present characteristics of an organism are determined very precisely by the characteristics of its parent or parents at the time when the reproduction process commenced. More frequently the Mendelian determination is only statistical. In all the mnemic laws an earlier event is said to determine a later event without the intervening causal chain being specified or indeed known. We may postulate, if we wish, persistent genes to explain the facts of heredity, and traces in the brain or unconscious ideas in the mind to explain memory; but these are extra explanatory hypotheses going beyond what the mnemic law itself states. Or we may follow Russell's suggestion of supposing that there is a type of causation (which he called "ultimate mnemic causation") in which a past event directly determines a future event without there being any intermediate causal chain. To suppose this would be almost as alien to our usual ways of thinking as to suppose that the future goal directly determines the present goal-directed action; and I agree with Russell in being unprepared to accept it if any way of escape is possible. As it is, physiologists are in the process of discovering strong independent evidence for the existence of the genes which the geneticists postulate; and the neurologists or the experimental and clinical psychologists may in time discover satisfactory independent evidence for cerebral traces or for a persistent Unconscious. But in the meantime we have our mnemic laws; and the best account of them seems to me to be given by treating them in exactly the same way as teleological laws and making the inductively

---

[16] *The Analysis of Mind*, pp. 77 ff.

inferred variancy the distinguishing feature. This variancy is frequently large in the case of mnemic laws as it is in teleological: Lashley's rats retained their acquired skill in running his maze after large, and different, portions of their brains had been removed.

Both teleological and mnemic laws, then, assert that there is a causal chain connecting the determining and the determined events which holds under a wide range of conditions, that is, that the system in question has a large variancy; and this variancy or plasticity has not been deduced from nonteleological or nonmnemic laws but has been established inductively by observation. The difference between them, that in a teleological law the determining event succeeds the determined event whereas in a mnemic law it precedes it, seems unimportant in comparison with their similarity; and I shall therefore class both types together under what I will for the lack of a better name call "biotic laws." I choose this name because the biotic laws which have struck our attention are those which apply to living systems, but my definition of "biotic law" includes no reference to life. Sometimes both a mnemic and a teleological law can be subsumed under one more general biotic law which is itself both mnemic and teleological: Mendel's laws of heredity state that characteristics of a set of organisms both are statistically determined by those of its set of parents and also statistically determine those of its set of offspring.[17]

This general notion of biotic law, of which teleological law is a species, is therefore offered as an attempt to settle the dispute between the biological "mechanists" and the biological "teleologists." But I fear that it will satisfy neither party. The teleologist will say that the whole account of teleological law in terms of causal chains and variancy of conditions presupposes the mechanist assumption that every event is physicochemically determined, and that to admit teleological explanations *faute de mieux* is to ignore the essentially irreducible character of teleological law for which he is contending. The mechanist will declare that he has no use for teleological laws unless they are ultimate and irreducible; and that it is methodologically vicious to introduce new types of law just because we do not know all the laws of nature of the ordinary type. And both parties will join forces in criticizing my treatment as being unduly epistemological: the controversy, they will both say, is not as to how we derive our knowledge of general propositions about goal-directed activity, but is about the content of these general propositions; it is a question of the ultimate elements in the biological facts, not of the organization of our present biological knowledge.

All these criticisms, and the joint one particularly, are based upon

---

[17] Rignano's inclusion of the "finalist manifestations of life" in a "mnemonic property" goes far beyond my simple comparison.

what must be regarded as a naïve attitude to the function of a scientific law. For this function is just exactly that of organizing our empirical knowledge so as to give both intellectual satisfaction and power to predict the unknown. The nature of scientific laws cannot be treated independently of their function within a deductive system. The world is not made up of empirical facts with the addition of the laws of nature: what we call the laws of nature are conceptual devices by which we organize our empirical knowledge and predict the future. From this point of view any general hypothesis whose consequences are confirmed by experience is a valuable intellectual device; and the profitable use of such a hypothesis does not presuppose that it will not at some future time be subsumed under some more general hypothesis in a more widely applicable deductive system, nor that the facts which it explains will not some time be explicable by a quite different hypothesis in another deductive system.

Biotic hypotheses behave exactly like other scientific hypotheses in that they can frequently be treated as lower-level hypotheses in a new deductive system in which they are deducible from a set of higher-level hypotheses. For example, the special teleological law about a particular food (for example, grass) as goal and a particular species of animal (for example, horses) is deducible from a less special teleological hypothesis about food-seeking in general together with biochemical hypotheses about the conditions for the digestibility of grass. Frequently one goal-directed activity in an animal (for example, the building of a nest) is followed by another type (for example, sitting on the eggs laid in the nest); and the succession of these two types of teleological activity falls under some general teleological law (for example, the mode of propagation of the species). Discussions as to the proper classification of instincts are largely discussions as to which is the best general deductive system containing higher-level biotic hypotheses for explaining the special instinctive modes of behavior. When E. S. Russell puts forward the generalization that "the goal of a directive action or series of actions is normally related to one or other of the main biological ends of maintenance, development, and reproduction," [18] he is suggesting that a deductive system whose highest-level hypotheses include teleological hypotheses about these three ends will be able to absorb all the systems which are in terms of particular goals. Of course none of these more elaborate deductive systems have been worked out in detail; but the possibility of constructing them makes teleological explanatory hypotheses like the nonteleological ones in another respect also, namely, that we can hope to provide further explanations, and a deeper intellectual satisfaction, by incorporating special laws in a unified system.

[18] *The Directiveness of Organic Activities,* p. 80.

I have given as part of the definition of a biotic law that it is not incorporated in a physicochemical deductive system.[19] But if such a law, already incorporated in a biotic deductive system (that is, one with biotic laws among its highest-level hypotheses), were to be found capable of physicochemical explanation, we should not by that mere fact be estopped from continuing to make use of its place in the biotic system whenever we found it profitable to think in this way. The chemical deductive system with Dalton's laws of atomic combination as highest-level hypotheses has in recent years been included more and more within the more general deductive system of physics; but chemists find it far more convenient to treat most of their problems in terms of atoms and molecules than in terms of electrons or wave-functions. And there is one feature of both teleological and mnemic explanations which will almost certainly make them continue to be useful (whatever they would then be called) even if they could be superseded by physicochemical ones. This feature is that usually teleological explanations make no reference to the exact length of time taken in attaining the goal, and mnemic explanations no reference to the exact length of time since the determining event. Indeed the unimportance of the time taken in reaching the goal is implicit in the persistency feature of goal-directed activity emphasized by biologists.[20] Teleological explanations do not specify the length of the causal chain, only that it attains the goal. So even if the biological mechanists can provide us with a complete explanation of life in physicochemical terms, we shall probably continue to give teleological (or what would previously have been called teleological) explanations whenever the exact time taken in reaching the goal does not interest us.

I will conclude this chapter by summarizing the biological part of the argument. An account has been given of the distinguishing feature of teleological explanations which does not assume that such explanations are ultimately irreducible to chemistry and physics and which does not require any novel concept of causal law. To do this I have followed biologists in emphasizing the plasticity of goal-directed behavior, and have analyzed the peculiarity of a teleological explanation in terms of the related notions of the multiplicity of the causal chains by which the goal may be attained and of the variety of conditions under which the goal-directed activity may occur. These notions have been found to be also involved in mnemic explanation. What has been drawn is only an outline sketch which will need much working upon to make a con-

---

[19] By this phrase is meant a deductive system whose highest-level hypotheses are physical or chemical.

[20] For example, E. S. Russell, *The Directiveness of Organic Activities*, p. 110: "If the goal is not reached, action usually persists."

vincing picture. But I have done enough to convince myself that what I have been trying to do is possible; and that the realm of biology will not have to sacrifice the autonomy proper to it if physics should succeed in establishing the claim, made by many biologists on its behalf, to be the Emperor of all the Natural Sciences.

THOUGHTS ON TELEOLOGY[1]

ISRAEL SCHEFFLER

INTRODUCTION:
TWO STRATEGIES IN INTERPRETING TELEOLOGY

How shall we relate teleological notions, referring events to certain of their consequences, with causal notions, referring events to certain of their antecedents? Two hard-headed strategies are discernible in the recent literature—hard-headed because in neither one are teleological statements taken to refer to special sorts of entities such as entelechies nor to embody special sorts of explanation by means of final causes. One such strategy is to interpret teleological statements as descriptions of plastic or self-regulating behavior, in principle explainable in ordinary causal terms. The other strategy is to construe ostensible mention of goals future to an action as referring rather to ideas of such goals prior to the action, and hence capable of figuring in its normal causal explanation.

"*Thoughts on Teleology,*" The British Journal for the Philosophy of Science, *Vol. IX, No. 59 (1958). Reprinted by permission of the author and Thomas Nelson and Sons, Ltd.*

[1] For certain critical suggestions, I am indebted to Professors N. Chomsky, N. Goodman, and M. Mandelbaum, who should not, however, be assumed to share the views presented here.

Each of these strategies has occasionally been used in such a way as to provoke the charge of misapplication. The first has thus, for the most part, been criticized for failing to do justice to purposive action in the higher animals and man, the second for unplausibly ascribing goal-ideas to the lower animals and to nonpurposive human behavior. These criticisms, however, leave unscathed a moderate use of either strategy within well-defined limits: so long as you do not try to reduce *purpose* to self-regulative behavior, nor attribute *ideas, wishes,* or *beliefs* to behavior that is not consciously purposive, you may proceed without hindrance.

It is this moderating assumption that I shall examine in the two main sections of the present paper: (i) First, with respect to two recent interpretations of teleology in terms of self-regulative behavior, I shall argue that they are inadequate not merely for purposive, but also for certain sorts of nonpurposive behavior, for which I will suggest the possibility of an alternative treatment. (ii) Secondly, I wish to indicate some serious logico-semantic difficulties attending purported references to beliefs about and desires for a goal even in accounting for fully purposive human action, and I want to explore a way of handling such difficulties.

1. THE SELF-REGULATION STRATEGY

(A) *Negative Feedback.* Perhaps the most basic recent paper applying the notion of self-regulation to the interpretation of teleology is that of Rosenblueth, Wiener, and Bigelow.[2] Convinced that "purposefulness [is] a concept necessary for the understanding of certain modes of behavior,"[3] and that its importance has been slighted as a result of the rejection of final causes, these authors propose to explain purpose, in largely engineering terms, as behavior "that may be interpreted as directed to the attainment of a goal, that is, to a final condition in which the behaving object reaches a definite correlation in time or in space with respect to another object or event."[4] In order to accomplish this explanation, the authors introduce the terms "input," "output," and "feedback," as follows. "Input" applies to events external to an object that modify the object in any manner. "Output," on the other hand, refers to changes produced in the surroundings by the object. "Feedback" may be used in two different ways. It may be applied to objects (such as electrical amplifiers), some of whose output energy is returned

---

[2] A. Rosenblueth, N. Wiener, and J. Bigelow, "Behaviour, Purpose, and Teleology," *Philosophy of Science,* Vol. X (1943). [See above, pp. 18 ff.]

[3] *Ibid.*

[4] *Ibid.*

as input. In such cases feedback is positive in that the output re-entering the object "has the same sign as the original input signal," [5] thus adding to this signal rather than correcting it. On the other hand, feedback is negative when the object's behavior is "controlled by the margin of error at which the object stands at a given time with reference to a relatively specific goal." [6] In such cases, "the signals from the goal are used to restrict outputs which would otherwise go beyond the goal." [7]

With the notion of negative feedback at hand, the authors propose that teleological behavior be construed as behavior controlled by negative feedback.[8] "All purposive behavior," they say, "may be considered to require negative feedback. If a goal is to be attained, some signals from the goal are necessary at some time to direct the behavior." [9] We may, of course, construct a machine that will impinge on a luminous object although the machine is insensitive to light, as well as to other stimuli emanating from the object. It would, however, be a mistake to consider such impingement behavior purposive inasmuch as "there are no signals from the goal which modify the activity of the object *in the course of the behavior.*" [10]

By contrast, some machines are "intrinsically purposeful," for example, "a torpedo with a target-seeking mechanism." [11] The behavior of such objects involves "a continuous feedback from the goal that modifies and guides the behaving object." [12] The path followed by the torpedo, for example, is controlled by the signals it receives from the moving target.

The foregoing conception of teleology is one whose scientific and practical importance is generally acknowledged and is surely not in question here. That it nevertheless fails adequately to characterize clear instances of purposive behavior is an independent point that emerges from the following considerations.

The authors interpret purposive behavior as directed toward "a final condition" in which the object achieves correlation with respect to some other entity. Since they describe the goal of such behavior as something that emits signals guiding the behaving object, the goal cannot be identified with the final condition of correlation mentioned above. For one thing, this final condition, if it occurs at all, is later than the

---

[5] *Ibid.*
[6] *Ibid.*
[7] *Ibid.*
[8] *Ibid.*
[9] *Ibid.*
[10] *Ibid.*, italics in original text.
[11] *Ibid.*
[12] *Ibid.*

behavior in question and cannot therefore be supposed to guide it if the notion of final causes acting upon earlier events is rejected. For another, the authors describe cases of "undamped feedback," in which a purposive machine, by increasingly larger oscillations, overshoots the mark and fails to attain the final condition toward which its behavior is directed, though such behavior has presumably been modified by signals from the goal. The goal, as described by these authors, cannot, therefore, be identified with the final condition of correlation and must rather be construed as that with which correlation is supposed to occur, that is, what we may call "the goal-object." This goal-object, even where correlation fails to occur, emits signals that modify the purposive activity of the behaving object.

The Difficulty of the Missing Goal-object

Now it is just the existence of such a goal-object that cannot be assumed in all cases of purposive behavior. As pointed out in a critical paper by R. Taylor,[13] a man's purpose in groping about in the dark may be to find matches that are not there, his purpose in going to the refrigerator may be to obtain a nonexistent apple, he may seek the philosopher's stone, the holy grail, the fountain of youth, or a live pulsing unicorn. In every such case his behavior is clearly purposive and yet in none is this behavior guided by signals emitted from a goal-object, correlation with which represents the final condition toward which the behavior is directed. Generally, if a man's purpose is to obtain object O, we cannot infer the existence of something x, identical with O, such that he seeks x, nor can we infer, from the fact that a man's purpose is to obtain something of kind K, that there exists some object of kind K for which he strives.[14]

This criticism, it will be noted, establishes the inadequacy of the Rosenblueth-Wiener-Bigelow interpretation only with respect to purposive cases. Indeed, Taylor supposes that we have here an "irreducible difference" between human beings and machines,[15] suggesting thereby that what may be called "the difficulty of the missing goal-object" does not arise for nonpurposive cases on the Rosenblueth-Wiener-Bigelow account. As against this suggestion, I now argue that the same difficulty

---

[13] R. Taylor, "Purposeful and Non-Purposeful Behavior: A Rejoinder," *Philosophy of Science*, Vol. XVII (1950), 329. [See above, pp. 17 ff.]

[14] Such inferences, invalid in cases where we have an apparent reference to a goal-object, cannot even be formulated naturally for purposive cases lacking such reference. The mystic striving to become more humble through spiritual training is not moving toward correlation with some object, guided by signals emanating from it.

[15] *Op. cit.,* p. 330.

arises also with respect to nonpurposive teleological behavior in non-human as well as human organisms, and conceivably in machines too.

Consider a standing passenger thrusting his foot outwards suddenly in order to keep his balance in a moving train, a rat depressing the lever in his experimental box in order to secure a food pellet, a small infant crying in order to attract mother's attention. To describe each of these cases as has just been done is to provide a teleological account relating the behavior in question to some selected end. It is not, however, to attribute purpose to the organism concerned, in the sense of our previous instances, for example. If the knight's purpose in traveling far and wide is to find the holy grail, he has chosen to search for it in the hope of finding it. If a man's purpose in opening the refrigerator door is to get an apple within, he opens it with the intention of getting an apple within. It would in most cases be peculiar, however, to describe the train-rider's sudden kick as a product of choice or as an expression of intention. Psychologists, similarly, often feel uncomfortable in describing the rat as choosing to depress the lever, or as depressing it with the intention of securing a pellet. Finally, we should not generally say of a small infant, even when it cries in order to attract mother, that it has chosen to cry with the intention of attracting mother—though it may of course do the latter at a later stage, when its crying will be interpreted quite differently by its elders. I suggest these cases merely as examples of a large group for which we willingly offer teleological accounts but withhold ascriptions of intention, choice, and purpose.

It does not take much reflection to see that the difficulty of the missing goal-object arises even for the moderate attempt to apply the Rosenblueth-Wiener-Bigelow interpretation to this set of nonpurposive cases. For we cannot plausibly suppose our train-rider to be receiving guiding signals from some region with which his foot is to be correlated. Neither, when the psychologist stops replacing the rat's pellets, can we describe the rat as receiving directive signals from some such pellet. Nor, finally, when mother, expecting baby to sleep, steps out to the corner store, is she available for the issuing of signals guiding the infant's behavior toward final correlation with herself. The Rosenblueth-Wiener-Bigelow analysis cannot therefore be judged generally adequate even for nonpurposive teleological behavior, nor does it seem to suffice even when we restrict ourselves to nonhuman cases.

Teleology and Learning

A suggestion: For at least *some* nonpurposive cases, I suggest that an interpretation in terms of learning may throw some light on teleological description, where analyses in terms of self-regulation fail. In the case of the infant, the suggestion is that our "in order to"-description of its present crying reflects our belief that this crying has been learned as a result of the consequences of like behavior in the past—more particularly, as a result of having received mother's attention. Having initially cried as a result of internal conditions C, and having thereby succeeded in attaining motherly solace, representing a type of rewarding effect E, the infant now cries in the absence of C, and as a result of several past learning sequences of C followed by E. The infant's crying has thus been divorced from its original conditions through the operation of certain of its past effects.[16] These past effects, though following their respective crying intervals, nonetheless precede the present crying interval which they help to explain. The apparent future-reference of a teleological description of this present interval is thus not to be confused with prediction, nor even with mention of particular objects in the current environment, toward which the behavior is directed. Rather, the teleological statement tells us something of the genesis of the present crying, and in particular, of the prominent role played by certain past consequences in this genesis. Such an account is perfectly compatible with normal causal explanation, and it indicates why goal-objects may very well be missing in some cases for which teleological description is appropriate. It shows also that we have in this respect no irreducible difference between human beings and machines, since machines capable of learning through the effects of their own operations are equally subject to such teleological description.

(B) *Plasticity of Behavior*. The interpretation of teleology proposed by R. B. Braithwaite,[17] though it resembles the Rosenblueth-Wiener-Bigelow approach, is considerably different in detail and restricts itself explicitly to what Braithwaite calls "goal-directed behavior" as distinct from "goal-intended behavior," [18] thus avoiding criticisms such as that of Taylor, based on purposive cases. Braithwaite's use of the self-regulation strategy is deliberately moderate; he wants to interpret "all teleological explanations which are not reducible to explanations in terms of a conscious intention to attain the goal." [19]

That the notion of *causal chains* is fundamental in the analysis of teleology is, for Braithwaite, shown by the fact that the organism's behavior does not directly produce the goal; it constitutes, rather, part of a causal sequence of events progressing toward the goal. What, however, distinguishes teleological causal chains from all others with which science is concerned? Here Braithwaite follows E. S. Russell in proposing as the main clue "the active persistence of directive activity towards

---

[16] R. S. Peters, "Symposium: Motives and Causes," *Proceedings of the Aristotelian Society*, Supp. Vol. XXVI (1952).

[17] *Scientific Explanation*, pp. 319 ff. [See above, pp. 27 ff.]

[18] *Ibid.*, p. 325.

[19] *Ibid.*

its goal, the use of alternative means towards the same end, the achievement of results in the face of difficulties." [20] Such plasticity of behavior
is "not in general a property of one teleological causal chain alone: it
is a property of the organism with respect to a certain goal, namely that
the organism can attain the same goal under different circumstances by
alternative forms of activity making use frequently of different causal
chains." [21] To specify this plasticity further, Braithwaite provides a
schematic description.

We have, let us suppose, some object b which, in the normal case,
is to be taken as a physical or organic system. Every event at any time
in b is assumed determined by the whole preceding state of b taken
together with the set of actual field or environmental conditions causally relevant to this event. Consider now a causal chain c, comprised
of events in the system b during a particular interval and following
immediately upon the initial state e of the system. Suppose also that the
set of actual field-conditions causally relevant to the events comprising
the chain is f. Then c is uniquely determined by the initial state e taken
together with the set of field-conditions f.

Causal chains may now be related to a goal, gamma, as follows.
Every chain ending in a gamma-event without containing any other
such event is a gamma-goal-attaining chain. Relative to a given initial
state e of b, we may consider the class of all (possible) sets of field-
conditions f uniquely determining chains that are gamma-goal-attaining.
This class is the variancy phi, with respect to b, e, and gamma, comprising the "range of circumstances under which the system attains the
goal." [22]

Plasticity may be attributed to the system when the variancy has
more than one member, so that the goal may be attained under alternative environmental circumstances, though not necessarily by means of
alternative causal chains. Teleological explanations assert that the
behavior in question is plastic, and are intellectually valuable to the
extent that this plasticity is not asserted on the basis of known causal
laws of the system's mechanism, but rather on the basis of past observation of the conditions under which similar behavior has taken place.
Further, teleological explanations predict the occurrence of some
gamma-goal-attaining chain on the basis of knowledge of the system's
plasticity; they predict, in other words, that the set of field-conditions

---

[20] Quoted from E. S. Russell, *The Directiveness of Organic Activities*, p. 144,
by Braithwaite, *op. cit.*, p. 329.

[21] Braithwaite, *op. cit.*, p. 329.

[22] *Ibid.*, p. 330: I do not discuss at length the problem of determining the
beginnings of goal-attaining chains, on this view. Strictly, according to the
definition given, a cat's capture of its first mouse ends a single mouse-attaining
chain that began with the birth of the cat.

that will in fact occur is a member of the appropriate variancy phi, on the ground that phi includes the class psi of all sets of field-conditions likely to occur.

It is at once apparent that, since Braithwaite does not construe goal-direction in terms of a relation to some goal-object but rather in terms of the variability of appropriate field circumstances, the difficulty of the missing goal-object does not arise in his scheme. Fido's pawing at the door need not be controlled by signals from outside; it need only lead to his being let out under alternative circumstances, say when his master is at home or when only his master's young son is at home. The rat need not, as he depresses the lever, be receiving any stimuli from the pellet that drops into his cup only after the lever is depressed; it is enough that his depressing of the lever results in his obtaining the pellet under a variety of experimental conditions.

The Difficulty of Goal-failure

Braithwaite's interpretation is, however, subject to other difficulties. For he appears to hold that particular teleological explanations do not merely ascribe plasticity to the behavior being explained but also predict goal-attainment in the circumstances that will in fact ensue. It is perhaps the least of the difficulties of this view that its use of the term "explanation" is strange, bearing little relation to normal causal explanation. Of crucial importance, however, is the fact that teleological descriptions, whether or not they qualify for the title "explanation," do not generally predict the attainment of the goal indicated. It is interesting that, despite the requirement of Rosenblueth, Wiener, and Bigelow for a *goal-object,* they allow for nonattainment or *goal-failure* in their examples of undamped feedback resulting in overshooting the target. But it is easy to multiply other examples of goal-failure. If Fido, trapped in a cave-in, is in fact never reached, is it therefore false that he pawed at the door in order to be let out? If, as in the case previously described, the psychologist stops replacing the consumed pellets with new ones, is it false to say the rat continues to depress the lever in order to obtain a pellet? To suppose, with Braithwaite, that all teleological explanations carry with them an "inference that the set of relevant conditions that will in fact occur in the future will fall within the variancy" [23] is to answer the preceding questions affirmatively and quite unplausibly.

The difficulty of goal-failure may, of course, be avoided if the prediction of goal-attainment is eliminated from the content of teleological descriptions. Retaining the rest of Braithwaite's scheme, we should then

---

[23] *Ibid.,* p. 334.

take such descriptions simply as attributing plasticity to the behavior in question with respect to the goal indicated. We should be saying of the system b exhibiting the state e that there is more than one possible set of field-conditions f, such that, were f conjoined with e, some suitable goal-attaining chain would ensue. We should not, however, be predicting that one of these sets will in fact be presently realized, and our statement would therefore be protected from falsification through goal-failure.

The Difficulty of Multiple Goals

This proposal is, however, immediately confronted with a new difficulty that we may call "the difficulty of multiple goals"; the proposal becomes too inclusive to differentiate between acceptable and inacceptable teleological descriptions in an indefinitely large number of cases. These cases may be indicated schematically in Braithwaite's terms. Imagine that for the system b, and relative to the present state e of this system, the class of those sets of field-conditions f uniquely determining gamma-goal-attaining chains has more than one member. The system in state e is thus plastic with respect to gamma. Suppose, now, that the class of those sets of field conditions f uniquely determining delta-goal-attaining chains relative to b and e also has more than one member. The same system in state e is thus also plastic with respect to delta. If our teleological description of the system's present behavior embodies neither a prediction of the attainment of gamma nor a prediction of the attainment of delta but restricts itself merely to an assertion of the plasticity of this behavior, we should be able, with equal warrant, to frame our teleological description either relative to gamma or relative to delta. We should, that is, be able to say either that b exhibits e in order to attain gamma or that b exhibits e in order to attain delta. This is, however, exactly what we cannot generally say.

The cat crouching before the vacant mouse-hole is crouching there in order to catch a mouse. Since no mouse is present, there will in fact be no goal-attainment. Nevertheless, the cat's behavior is plastic since there are various hypothetical sets of field-conditions, each set including one condition positing a mouse within the cat's range, such that, in conjunction with the cat's present behavior, each set determines a mouse-attaining causal chain. On the other hand, there are also various other hypothetical sets of field-conditions, each set including one positing a bowl of cream within the cat's range, such that, conjoined to the cat's present behavior, each set determines a cream-attaining causal chain. It should therefore be a matter of complete indifference, so far as the present proposal is concerned, whether we describe the cat as crouching before the mouse-hole in order to catch a mouse or as crouching before the mouse-hole in order to get some cream. The fact that we reject the latter teleological description while accepting the former is a fact that the present proposal cannot explain.

A limiting case of this difficulty occurs when the state e is one for which we should reject *every* positive teleological description. Imagine, for example, that e is the state of physical exhaustion and that the relevant class of field-condition sets is the one just considered in connection with mouse-attainment, suitably supplemented by conditions stipulating the cat's recuperation and assumption of a crouching position before the mouse-hole. The present proposal would then warrant us in saying, absurdly, that the cat is physically exhausted in order to catch a mouse.

Other examples of the difficulty of multiple goals arise in cases where every gamma-goal-attaining chain is also a delta-goal-attaining chain or contains such a chain as a part, so that if the variancy with respect to gamma has more than one member, so has the variancy with respect to delta. Consider, for example, an infant crying in order to get mother's cuddling, which is always preceded by the sound of mother's footsteps. Since every set of field-conditions determining a cuddling chain in this situation also determines a footstep chain, and since we may assume the class of such sets determining cuddling chains to have more than one member, we may infer that the class of sets determining footstep chains also has more than one member. Thus we should again be warranted by the present proposal in saying either that the infant cries in order to receive its mother's cuddling or that it cries in order to hear mother's footsteps. The proposal again proves itself too inclusive to differentiate between teleological descriptions we accept and those we reject.

The Learning Suggestion Again: A Caution

Can the wanted distinctions be made on the basis of the learning interpretation suggested earlier? The answer seems to be "yes" with regard to the examples we have considered. Thus we do not believe the cat has learned to crouch before the mouse-hole as a result of having been rewarded with a bowl of cream for having done so in the past. Nor do we suppose the infant's crying to have been learned as a result of having heard its mother's footsteps following past crying intervals. Nevertheless, I *surely do not* wish to propose the learning interpretation as an adequate analysis simply on the basis of a few examples and I am convinced, moreover, that several lines of interpretation will be required to account for the variety of statements commonly labeled "teleological." Furthermore, to appeal to our beliefs as to how the behavior in question has been learned is, I think, to provide no firm philosophical answer: it is rather to suggest the importance of addressing our critical attention to the field of learning.

2. THE GOAL-IDEA STRATEGY

Background and Formulation

The second strategy mentioned at the outset consists, it will be recalled, in replacing reference to *goals* future to an action by reference to prior *ideas of such goals* functioning as causes of the action. What is the motive for this strategy? Suppose we explain John's decision to take a premedical course by saying that he decided to do so in order to enter medical school. Of what explanatory value is the apparent reference to John's future entrance? If it indeed comes to pass, it follows his present curricular decision and so cannot be among its causes. On the other hand, if it never comes to pass—for example, if John fails to complete his premedical training, we surely cannot count such entrance as a cause or partial cause of his actual decision. If the brick in fact did *not* strike the window, we cannot well say the window shattered because of the impact of the brick. What sense shall we then make of the fact that, although John's entrance to medical school is possibly fictional and, in any event, future to his decision, he clearly did choose his premedical course in order to enter medical school at a later date? The natural, and quite plausible, suggestion is to say that John's prior *desire* to enter, and his prior *belief* that entrance is contingent on choice of a premedical course, jointly determine his choice. Even if his desire is in the end thwarted and his belief in fact false, they are nevertheless realities of the situation preceding his choice, and they contribute, moreover, to its causal determination.

This strategy, quite plausible in the case just considered, has been rightly criticized in numerous others for projecting belief and desire into phenomena without adequate justification. As Ducasse has put it,

> the disrepute into which teleological explanations have fallen is doubtless due to their having been so frequently thus put forth in cases where the existence of the agent appealed to and of his beliefs and desires was not already known, but invented outright and purely *ad hoc*. . . . But when antecedent evidence for their existence is present (for example, when the hypothetical agent is a human being), a teleological explanation is methodologically quite respectable, although, like any other, it may in a given case not happen to be the correct one.[24]

---

[24] C. J. Ducasse, "Explanation, Mechanism, and Teleology," *Journal of Philosophy,* Vol. XXIII (1926). Reprinted in Feigl and Sellars, *Readings in Philosophical Analysis* (New York: Appleton-Century-Crofts, Inc., 1949), pp. 543-544.

Accordingly, Ducasse suggests the following as essential elements in genuine cases of purpose, rendering teleological explanation possible in the form exemplified by our recent illustration:

1. *Belief* by the performer of the act in a law . . . for example, that if X occurs, Y occurs [or that Y is contingent upon X].
2. *Desire* by the performer that Y shall occur.
3. *Causation by that desire and that belief jointly,* of the performance of X.[25]

The sort of rule allowing explanation of the occurrence of X is further suggested by Ducasse as "If an agent believes that Y is contingent upon X and desires Y, then that agent is likely to do X." [26]

Now, even if we restrict the present strategy to clearly purposive human action in the sense specified by Ducasse, for example, we face serious problems in formulating the required explanatory statements. By way of illustration, let us try to explain John's curricular choice according to some such schema as that suggested by Ducasse. We ask, "Why does John choose a premedical course?", and we receive the following statements in reply:

(i) John desires John's entrance to medical school.
(ii) John believes that John's entrance to medical school is contingent on John's choice of a premedical course.
(iii) Whenever someone desires something, believing that it is contingent on something else, he performs this other thing.

In symbols:

$$(x)\ (y)\ (z)\ ((x \text{ desires } y \ . \ x \text{ believes that } y$$
$$\text{contingent on } z) \supset x \text{ performs } z),$$

(with the range of the variable z restricted to acts or choices).

This sample explanation is obviously crude and oversimplified, raising numerous questions peripheral to the logico-semantic difficulties that are my present concern. Thus, for example, to say "John performs John's choice of a premedical course," in concluding our explanatory argument here, is indeed a violation of English but one that provides a uniform technique for describing action. More important is the fact that (iii) requires much qualification before it can be taken seriously as a truth of conduct. Nobody can perform every act upon which the fulfillment of his desires is believed to be contingent, for some such acts are beyond his power. Nor does anyone actually choose to do everything within his power that he believes necessary for the attainment of every one of his desires, even if the dictates of the latter are compatible. Nevertheless, if John's desire and belief are to figure in the causal ac-

---

[25] *Ibid.*, p. 543. Addition in brackets mine; this seems quite in line with Ducasse's intent.
[26] *Ibid.*

count of his choice, as the strategy we are considering requires, some generalization incorporating these three elements but considerably more complicated than (iii) must be supposed as a premise. Since any such generalization faces the same difficulties that I wish to indicate with reference to (iii), the latter statement may here be taken as a simple model for a general problem.

Logico-ontological Difficulties: Objects of Desire

We may begin by asking, "What is the intended range of the variable y in (iii)?" Surely this range is not limited to actual things for, as mentioned earlier, the argument is intended to hold even if John's entrance to medical school never comes to pass. As in the case of purpose discussed earlier, we cannot infer existence of the objects of desire. To expand the range of y to include possible but nonactual entities is not, moreover, sufficient, for the squaring of the circle and other impossibles have undoubtedly been desired. Allowing the variable y to range over impossible so-called things as well is a step not many are prepared to take. It is bad enough to have to say, "There is a possible but nonactual pot of gold at the end of the rainbow which has been desired by men," but to say, "There exists a nonactual and, moreover, impossible squaring of the circle which has been desired by many" puts an impossible strain on the word "exists," to say the very least.

Logico-ontological Difficulties: Belief

The variable y, furthermore, appears not only in the context x desires y," but also in the context "x believes that y contingent on z," and both y and z refer back to prefixed quantifiers. Such quantification into belief contexts is, as Quine has repeatedly warned, a problematic procedure.[27] The occurrence of singular terms within belief contexts is, as he puts it, not purely referential in that the truth of such contexts taken as wholes depends not merely on the objects named by such terms but also on the manner of naming; belief contexts are, in short, referentially opaque. To use Quine's example, Philip may believe that Cicero denounced Catiline without believing that Tully denounced Catiline, though Cicero and Tully are identical. To replace either the name "Cicero" or the name "Tully" with a variable ranging over concrete objects such as people, in quantified belief sentences about Philip, thus yields an unintelligible result, since Philip's belief cannot be

---

[27] W. V. Quine, "Notes on Existence and Necessity," *Journal of Philosophy,* Vol. XL (1943), 113 ff.; Chap. 8 of *From a Logical Point of View* (Cambridge, Mass.: Harvard University Press, 1953); and "Quantifiers and Propositional Attitudes," *Journal of Philosophy,* Vol. LXI (1956), 177 ff.

interpreted as a relation between Philip, Cataline, and some man to whom the names "Cicero" and "Tully" equally apply.

Quine has indeed admitted with reference to modal contexts, which are also referentially opaque, that a suitable limitation of the ontology to objects not nameable by nonsynonymous names renders unrestricted quantification legitimate once more.[28] This result is due to the fact that interchangeability of synonymous names preserves truth value even within modal contexts, thus rendering the manner of naming again irrelevant and allowing modal statements to be true or false depending simply on the objects referred to. If, however, as I have elsewhere argued,[29] synonymy is not sufficient to guarantee interchangeability with preservation of truth value within belief contexts, the ontological restriction above mentioned will not legitimize quantification into *belief* contexts despite its adequacy for *modal* contexts. To be safe, we should need to restrict our ontology to objects not nameable by nonidentical names within our language. Instead of the concrete object Cicero, for example, we would now recognize as many objects in our new ontology as there are different names or descriptions of Cicero, whether synonymous or not. This seems a desperate expedient indeed, not to say a transparent projection of our language into the world of things.

Notice, finally, that the variable z occurs once within the belief context and once outside it, subject to the same external quantifier, thus serving to tie together the agent's act with his view of his act, as the variable y serves to tie together the agent's desire and his beliefs about the conditions of fulfillment of that desire. Waiving all questions as to the nature and individuation of such entities as acts, it should be noted that these connections between act, desire, and belief are essential not only to the strategy under consideration, but also to every developed conception of rational behavior. Indeed, if we have no way of formulating these connections in such a way as to avoid the difficulties discussed, we lack a satisfactory account of human action. The following remarks are devoted to the exploration of a possible solution.

Suggestion for an Inscriptional Interpretation

Suppose we try to construe desire, belief, and performance, at least with respect to the present schema, as relations between agents and inscriptions. The initial advantage to be hoped for is, of course, the relative clarity of inscriptions as concrete physical objects in comparison with the possibles, impossibles, and other strange entities posited by the

---

[28] W. V. Quine, *From a Logical Point of View*, pp. 150 ff.

[29] I. Scheffler, "On Synonymy and Indirect Discourse," *Philosophy of Science,* Vol. XXII (1955), 39 ff.

approaches we have so far considered. The existence of inscriptions is, furthermore, completely independent of the existence of their purported objects. Though no pot of gold dangles from the end of any rainbow, we cannot infer that no inscription affirms that there is such a pot of gold. Where an object of desire fails to exist, its purported description need not, correspondingly, fail to exist. Even where something lacks not only being but possibility, its nonexistence does not generally carry over to its purported description. To assert the existence of something both square and not square is a serious and offensive thing to do; to attribute being to some inscription asserting such existence is something else and quite innocuous. Can we reconstrue the explanatory argument (i)-(iii) in such a way as to capitalize on the advantages of an inscriptional formulation?

Desiring True

Suppose we begin by transforming (i) into the following statement, converting the singular term naming the object of John's desire into a clause:

> (I) John desires that John enter medical school.

Let us now construe this statement as:

> (i′) John desires-true some that-John-enters-medical-school inscription.

Desiring-true is here to be taken as a relation between people or other suitable agents on the one hand and inscriptions on the other, and does not require that the agent produce or even understand the inscription that he desires-true. To interpret this first premise of the explanatory argument as we have done can, moreover, be no more obscure than to construe it as relating John to some such entity as a hypothetical state of affairs named by the that-clause of the premise. For it is always possible to satisfy proponents of the latter construal by explaining the desiring-true of a given inscription as the desiring of that state of affairs which is named by it or by the proposition it expresses. The present interpretation, it should also be noted, treats the that-clause of (I) as a single predicate that applies to inscriptions peculiarly related to itself—inscriptions constituting rephrasals of its own sentential content, *including this very content as well*.[30] Thus (i′) tells us that

---

[30] See I. Scheffler, "An Inscriptional Approach to Indirect Quotation," *Analysis,* Vol. XIV (1957), 83 ff., for a fuller explanation of this general approach. The fact that the sentential content of the that-clause predicate is included in its application gurantees the existence of an appropriate inscription by the very existence of the stated premise.

John desires-true something which is a that-John-enters-medical-school. Every such thing, further, is an inscription rephrasing the "John enters medical school"-inscription that forms the content of the that-clause predicate of (i'). We shall, finally, make the assumption that to desire-true any given inscription denoted by a that-clause predicate is to desire-true every such inscription.

Believing True

Turning now to the second premise (ii) of our explanatory argument, let us first transform it into the following statement, eliminating reference to contingency in favor of a conditional of the type suggested by Ducasse:

(II) John believes that if John enters medical school then John chooses a premedical course.

Let us now interpret this statement as:

(ii') John believes-true some that-if-John-enters-medical-school-then-John-chooses-a-premedical-course inscription.

Believing-true[31] is, analogously with desiring-true, here taken to be a relation between agents and inscriptions, not implying that the agent produce or understand those inscriptions he believes-true. Such an interpretation is at least as clear as the usual construal of belief as a relation between a person and a proposition, for the believing-true of a given inscription is explicable to the intensionalist as the believing of the proposition expressed by it or by the statement it designates. The that-clause of (II) is to be treated also as a single unanalyzable predicate applicable to rephrasals of its own sentential content, *inclusive of such content*.[32] Finally, we are to assume that to believe-true some inscription denoted by a given that-clause predicate is to believe-true every inscription denoted by that predicate.

Making True

Turning now to the third premise required to complete our explanatory argument, let us replace the original (iii) with the following:

(iii') Whenever anyone x desires-true any inscription v and believes-true another inscription z, such that z is the conditional of v

---

[31] This relation is suggested by W. V. Quine, "Quantifiers and Propositional Attitudes," p. 186. Quine uses believing-true as a relation between agents and sentences, and thus expands it from a dyadic to a triadic relation, relativizing it to language.

[32] As with desiring-true, the existence of an appropriate inscription is guaranteed by the existence of the whole premise.

and a third inscription w, then x makes-true w. (Here the range of the variable w is restricted to English sentence-inscriptions of the form "x chooses. . . .")[33]

Making-true, similarly to desiring-true and believing-true, is a relation between agents and inscriptions and does not require the agent to produce or even to understand the inscriptions he makes-true. Making-true a given inscription can always, furthermore, be explained as performing the act described by the inscription or by its associated proposition; in the present case, John's making-true of a "John chooses a premedical course"-inscription is explicable as his performing of the choice described, as his doing of the act. We shall, further, suppose that to make-true a given inscription is to make-true every rephrasal of it. It should especially be noted that, unlike inscriptions desired-true or believed-true, every inscription made-true is in fact true, together with all its rephrasals.

Reformulation of the Teleological Argument

How shall we now explain John's choice of a premedical course with the aid of our reformulated premises? From (i′) we learn that John desires-true some inscription x to which the that-clause predicate of (i′) is applicable. This inscription x, we know, is a rephrasal of the content of this predicate itself. (ii′) conveys that John believes-true some inscription y denoted by the that-clause predicate of (ii′). Looking at this latter predicate of (ii′), we note that its sentential content is a conditional of which the antecedent is a *replica* of the content of the that-clause predicate of (i′). On the assumption that (i′) and (ii′) belong to the same language and contain no indicator terms, this antecedent must therefore also be a *rephrasal* of the that-clause content of (i′). If so, it must also be denoted by the that-clause predicate of (i′), that is, this antecedent must also be a that-John-enters-medical-school. Since, moreover, (i′) says that John desires-true *some* inscription x which is a that-John-enters-medical-school, he must also desire-true the antecedent in question. This follows because of our assumption that to desire-true any inscription denoted by a given that-clause predicate is to desire-true every such inscription.

Now y, which John believes-true according to (ii′), is denoted by its that-clause predicate. But we know that the content of this predicate itself is also so denoted. Thus we may conclude that John believes-

---

[33] Strictly, other restrictions on this range would be needed to prevent awkward results. It might be best, for example, to restrict the vocabulary and syntax of such inscriptions in certain ways. But I am concentrating on the general idea here and so do not enter into details.

true this very content itself, that is, the conditional inscription of (ii′). This conclusion, it will be recalled, is warranted by our assumption that to believe-true any inscription denoted by a given that-clause predicate is to believe-true every inscription denoted by that predicate.

The conditional inscription of (ii′) believed-true by John is, however, the identical one of which we already know that John desires-true the antecedent. This conditional may thus be taken as the conditional z of (iii′), its antecedent may be taken as v in (iii′), and its consequent may then be taken as w of (iii′). The conclusion may now be drawn that John makes-true the consequent of the conditional in question as well as every one of its rephrasals. Since the consequent is made-true, it is in fact true, together with every one of its rephrasals. We may now, in particular, write down a replica of this consequent in the same language as our three premises. On the assumption that it contains no indicators, it will then also be a rephrasal of the consequent, hence true. It will thus represent the needed conclusion of our argument:

(iv′) John chooses a premedical course.

The foregoing analysis is only exploratory. It remains to be seen to what extent the treatment of our example can be generalized. If it proves sufficiently general, it will, by avoiding reference to desired states of affairs, believed propositions, and performed acts, have managed also to escape the semantical difficulties plaguing the second strategy we have considered. It does not, however, provide an "operational" definition of "belief," "desire," and "performance" idioms; thus believing-true, desiring-true, and making-true are, for all that we have said, no clearer *in application* than these original idioms themselves. Their explication presents an important problem left unsolved by our above treatment, which has addressed itself to specific semantic difficulties.

SUMMARY

1. Two strategies for interpreting teleology have been examined: the self-regulation strategy, and the goal-idea strategy. Criticism has been directed explicitly against the moderate use of each strategy, that is, the use of the first solely for nonpurposive behavior and the use of the second solely for purposive behavior.

2. Two basic variants of the self-regulation strategy have been criticized as inadequate to account for nonpurposive (let alone purposive) teleological behavior. (A) The inadequacy of the "negative feedback" variant has been discussed in connection with the difficulty of the missing goal-object. (B) The inadequacy of the "plasticity" variant has been argued by reference to the difficulty of goal-failure and the difficulty

of multiple goals. (C) These inadequacies are not, of course, taken as proving that the self-regulation strategy is never applicable, but only as showing that it is not sufficient, even for nonpurposive teleological behavior.

3. With respect to nonpurposive cases, another interpretation of teleology, in terms of learning, is suggested. (A) This interpretation construes the future-reference of teleological statements not as predictive nor as descriptive of objects in the current environment, but as pointing to the role of consequences in the genesis of the learned behavior in question. (B) The learning interpretation seems to avoid the difficulties previously discussed, but the matter both requires and deserves further study. (C) The learning interpretation is, in any event, proposed as only *one* among several that are likely to be needed.

4. The second (that is, goal-idea) strategy has been argued to involve logico-ontological difficulties in its natural formulation, which makes use of the notions of belief, desire, and performance. These difficulties hold even when the strategy is applied to clearly purposive cases.

5. An inscriptional proposal for avoiding these difficulties is explored. (A) This proposal makes use of the new notions "desiring-true," "believing-true," and "making-true," holding between agents and inscriptions. (B) A sample teleological explanation is reformulated in terms of these notions, to show how the argument may be carried through in a way that is both materially adequate and free of the logico-ontological difficulties mentioned earlier. (C) This proposal, too, requires further study, and is, in any event, not intended to give an *explication* or operational analysis of belief, desire, and performance.

TELEOLOGICAL

EXPLANATION

ERNEST NAGEL

THE STRUCTURE OF TELEOLOGICAL
EXPLANATIONS

Almost any biological treatise or monograph yields conclusive evidence
that biologists are concerned with the functions of vital processes and
organs in maintaining characteristic activities of living things. In consequence, if "teleological analysis" is understood to be an inquiry into
such functions, and into processes directed toward attaining certain
end-products, then undoubtedly teleological explanations are pervasive
in biology. In this respect, certainly, there appears to be a marked difference between biology and the physical sciences. It would surely be an
oddity on the part of a modern physicist were he to declare, for example, that atoms have outer shells of electrons in order to make
chemical unions between themselves and other atoms possible. In ancient
Aristotelian science, categories of explanations suggested by the study
of living things and their activities (and in particular by human art)
were made canonical for all inquiry. Since nonliving as well as living
phenomena were thus analyzed in teleological terms—an analysis which

From The Structure of Science *by Ernest Nagel,* © *1961, by Harcourt, Brace*
& World, Inc. and reprinted with their permission.

made the notion of final cause focal—Greek science did not assume a fundamental cleavage between biology and other natural science. Modern science, on the other hand, regards final causes to be vestal virgins which bear no fruit in the study of physical and chemical phenomena; and, because of the association of teleological explanations with the doctrine that goals or ends of activity are dynamic agents in their own realizations, it tends to view such explanations as a species of obscurantism. But does the presence of teleological explanations in biology and their apparent absence from the physical sciences entail the absolute autonomy of the former? We shall try to show that it does not.

1. Quite apart from their association with the doctrine of final causes, teleological explanations are sometimes suspect in modern natural science because they are assumed to invoke purposes or ends-in-view as causal factors in natural processes. Purposes and deliberate goals admittedly play important roles in human activities, but there is no basis whatever for assuming them in the study of physicochemical and most biological phenomena. However, as has already been noted, a great many explanations counted as teleological do not postulate any purposes or ends-in-view; for explanations are often said to be "teleological" only in the sense that they specify the *functions* which things or processes possess. Most contemporary biologists certainly do not impute purposes to the organic parts of living things whose functions are investigated; most of them would probably also deny that the means-ends relationships discovered in the organization of living creatures are the products of some deliberate plan on the part of a purposeful agent, whether divine or in some other manner supranatural. To be sure, there are biologists who postulate psychic states as concomitants and even as directive forces of all organic behavior. But such biologists are in a minority; and they usually support their views by special considerations that can be distinguished from the facts of functional or teleological dependencies which most biologists do not hesitate to accept. Since the word "teleology" is ambiguous, confusion and misunderstandings would doubtless be prevented if the word were eliminated from the vocabulary of biology. But biologists do use it, and say they are giving a teleological explanation when, for example, they explain that the function of the alimentary canal in vertebrates is to prepare ingested materials for absorption into the bloodstream. The crucial point is that when biologists do employ teleological language they are not necessarily committing the pathetic fallacy or lapsing into anthropomorphism.

We shall therefore assume that teleological (or functional) statements in biology normally neither assert nor presuppose in the materials under discussion either manifest or latent purposes, aims, objectives, or goals. Indeed, it seems safe to suppose that biologists would generally deny they are postulating any conscious or implicit ends-in-view even when they employ such words as "purpose" in their functional analyses—as when the "purpose" (that is, the function) of kidneys in the pig is said to be that of eliminating various waste products from the bloodstream of the organism. On the other hand, we shall adopt as the mark of a teleological statement in biology, and as the feature that distinguishes such statements from nonteleological ones, the occurrence in the former but not in the latter of such typical locutions as "the function of," "the purpose of," "for the sake of," "in order that," and the like—more generally, the occurrence of expressions signifying a means-ends nexus.

Nevertheless, despite the *prima facie* distinctive character of teleological (or functional) explanations, we shall first argue that they can be reformulated, without loss of asserted content, to take the form of nonteleological ones, so that in an important sense teleological and nonteleological explanations are equivalent. To this end, let us consider a typical teleological statement in biology, for example, "The function of chlorophyll in plants is to enable plants to perform photosynthesis (that is, to form starch from carbon dioxide and water in the presence of sunlight)." This statement accounts for the presence of chlorophyll (a certain substance A) in plants (in every member S of a class of systems, each of which has a certain organization C of component parts and processes). It does so by declaring that, when a plant is provided with water, carbon dioxide, and sunlight (when S is placed in a certain "internal" and "external" environment E), it manufactures starch (a certain process P takes place yielding a definite product or outcome) only if the plant contains chlorophyll. The statement usually carries with it the additional tacit assumption that without starch the plant cannot continue its characteristic activities, such as growth and reproduction (it cannot maintain itself in a certain state G); but for the present we shall ignore this further claim.

Accordingly, the teleological statement is a telescoped argument, so that when the content is unpacked it can be rendered approximately as follows: When supplied with water, carbon dioxide, and sunlight, plants produce starch; if plants have no chlorophyll, even though they have water, carbon dioxide, and sunlight, they do not manufacture starch; hence, plants contain chlorophyll. More generally, a teleological statement of the form "The function of A in a system S with organization C is to enable S in environment E to engage in process P" can be formulated more explicitly by: Every system S with organization C and in environment E engages in process P; if S with organization C and in environment E does not have A, then S does not engage in P; hence, S with organization C must have A.

It is clearly not relevant in the present context to inquire whether the premises in this argument are adequately supported by competent evidence. However, because the issue is sometimes raised in discussions of teleological explanations, at least passing notice deserves to be given to the question of whether chlorophyll is really necessary to plants and whether they could not manufacture starch (or other substances essential for their maintenance) by some alternative process not requiring chlorophyll. For, if the presence of chlorophyll is not actually necessary for the production of starch (or if plants can maintain themselves without the mechanism of photosynthesis), so it has been urged, the second premise in the above argument is untenable. The premise would then have to be modified; and in its emended form it would assert that chlorophyll is an element in a set of conditions that is *sufficient* (but not necessary) for the production of starch. In that case, however, the new argument with the emended premise would be invalid, so that the proposed teleological explanation of the presence of chlorophyll in plants would apparently be unsatisfactory.

This objection is in part well-taken. It is certainly *logically* possible that plants might maintain themselves without manufacturing starch, or that processes in living organisms might produce starch without requiring chlorophyll. Indeed, there are plants (the funguses) that can flourish without chlorophyll; and in general, there is more than one way of skinning a cat. On the other hand, the above teleological explanation of the occurrence of chlorophyll in plants is presumably concerned with living organisms having certain determinate forms of organization and definite modes of behavior—in short, with the so-called "green plants." Accordingly, although living organisms (plants as well as animals) capable of maintaining themselves without processes involving the operation of chlorophyll are both abstractly and physically possible, there appears to be no evidence whatever that in view of the limited capacities green plants possess as a consequence of their *actual* mode of organization, these organisms can live without chlorophyll.

Two important complementary points thus emerge from these considerations. In the first place, teleological analyses in biology (or in other sciences in which such analyses are pursued) are not explorations of merely logical possibilities, but deal with the actual functions of definite components in concretely given living systems. In the second place, on pain of failure to recognize the possibility of alternative mechanisms for achieving some end-product, and of unwittingly (and perhaps mistakenly) assuming that a process known to be indispensable in a given class of systems is also indispensable in a more inclusive class, a teleological explanation must articulate with exactitude both the character of the end-product and the defining traits of the systems manifesting them, relative to which the indicated processes are supposedly indispensable.

In any event, however, the above teleological account of chlorophyll, in its expanded form, is simply an illustration of an explanation that conforms to the deductive model, and contains no locution distinctive of teleological statements. Accordingly, the initial, unexpanded statement about chlorophyll appears to assert nothing that is not asserted by "Plants perform photosynthesis only if they contain chlorophyll," or alternatively by "A necessary condition for the occurrence of photosynthesis in plants is the presence of chlorophyll." These latter statements do not explicitly ascribe a function to chlorophyll, and in that sense are therefore not teleological formulations. If this example is taken as a paradigm, it seems that, when a function is ascribed to a constituent element in an organism, the content of the teleological statement is fully conveyed by another statement that is not explicitly teleological and that simply asserts a necessary (or possibly a necessary and sufficient) condition for the occurrence of a certain trait or activity of the organism. In the light of this analysis, therefore, a teleological explanation in biology indicates the *consequences* for a given biological system of a constituent part or process; the equivalent nonteleological formulation of this explanation, on the other hand, states some of the *conditions* (sometimes, but not invariably, in physicochemical terms) under which the system persists in its characteristic organization and activities. The difference between a teleological explanation and its equivalent nonteleological formulation is thus comparable to the difference between saying that Y is an effect of X, and saying that X is a cause or condition of Y. In brief, the difference is one of selective attention, rather than of asserted content.

This point can be reinforced by another consideration. If a teleological explanation had an asserted content different from the content of every conceivable nonteleological statement, it would be possible to cite procedures and evidence employed for establishing the former that differ from the procedures and evidence required for warranting the latter. But in point of fact there appear to be no such procedures and evidence. Consider, for example, the teleological statement "The function of the leucocytes in human blood is to defend the body against foreign microorganisms." Now whatever may be the evidence that warrants this statement, that evidence also confirms the nonteleological statement "Unless human blood contains a sufficient number of leucocytes, certain normal activities of the body are impaired," and conversely. If this is so, however, there is a strong presumption that the two statements do not differ in factual content. More generally, if, as seems to be the case, the conceivable evidence for any given teleological explanation is identical with the conceivable evidence for a certain nonteleological one, the conclusion appears inescapable that those statements cannot be distinguished with respect to what they *assert,* even though they are distinguishable in other ways.

2. This proposed equation of teleological and nonteleological explanations must nevertheless face a fundamental objection. Many biologists would perhaps admit that a teleological statement *implies* a certain nonteleological one; but some of them, at any rate, are prepared to maintain that the latter statement generally does not in turn imply the former one, and that in consequence the alleged equivalence between the statements does not in fact hold.

The claim that there is indeed no such equivalence can be forcefully presented as follows. If there were such an equivalence, not only could a teleological explanation be replaced by a nonteleological one, but conversely a nonteleological explanation could also be replaced by a teleological one. In consequence, the customary statements of laws and theories in the physical sciences would be translatable without change in asserted content into teleological formulations. In point of fact, however, modern physical science does not appear to sanction such reformulations. Indeed, most physical scientists would doubtless resist the introduction of teleological statements into their disciplines as a misguided attempt to reinstate the point of view of Greek and medieval science. For example, the statement "The volume of a gas at constant temperature varies inversely with its pressure" is a typical physical law, which is entirely free of teleological connotations. If it were equivalent to a teleological statement, its equivalent (constructed on the model of the example adopted above as paradigmatic) would presumably be "The function of a varying pressure in a gas at constant temperature is to produce an inversely varying volume of the gas," or perhaps "Every gas at constant temperature under a variable pressure alters its volume in order to keep the product of the pressure and the volume constant." But most physicists would undoubtedly regard these formulations as preposterous, and at best as misleading. Accordingly, if no teleological statement can correctly translate a law of physics, the contention that for every teleological statement a logically equivalent nonteleological one can be constructed seems hardly tenable. There must therefore be some important difference between teleological and nonteleological statements, so the objection concludes, that the discussion has thus far failed to make explicit.

The difficulty just expounded cannot be disposed of easily. To assess it adequately, we must consider the type of subject matter in which teleological analyses are currently undertaken, and in which teleological explanations are not rejected ostensibly as a matter of general principle.

a. The attitude of physical scientists toward teleological formulations in their disciplines is doubtless as alleged in this objection. Nevertheless, this fact is not completely decisive on the point at issue. Two comments are in order which tend to weaken its critical force.

In the first place, it is not entirely accurate to maintain that the physical sciences never employ formulations that have at least the appearance of teleological statements. As is well known, some physical laws and theories are often expressed in so-called "isoperimetric" or "variational" form, rather than in the more familiar manner of numerical or differential equations. When laws and theories are expressed in this fashion, they strongly resemble teleological formulations, and have in fact been frequently assumed to express a teleological ordering of events and processes. For example, an elementary law of optics states that the angle of incidence of a light ray reflected by a surface is equal to the angle of reflection. However, this law can also be rendered by the statement that a light ray travels in such a manner that the length of its actual path (from its source to reflecting surface to its terminus) is the minimum of all possible paths. More generally, a considerable part of classical as well as contemporary physical theory can be stated in the form of "extremal" principles. These principles assert that the actual development of a system proceeds in such a manner as to minimize or maximize some magnitude which represents the possible configurations of the system.[1]

The discovery that the principles of mechanics can be given such extremal formulations was once considered as evidence for the operation of a divine plan throughout nature. This view was made prominent by Maupertuis, an eighteenth-century thinker who was perhaps the first to state mechanics in variational form; and it was widely accepted in the eighteenth and nineteenth centuries. Such theological interpretations of extremal principles are now almost universally recognized to be entirely gratuitous; and with rare exceptions, physicists today do not accept the earlier claim that extremal principles entail the assumption of a plan or purpose animating physical processes. The use of such principles in physical science nevertheless does show that the dynamical structure of physical systems can be formulated so as to make focal the effect of constituent elements and subsidiary processes upon certain global properties of the system taken as a whole. If physical scientists dislike teleological language in their own disciplines, it is not because they regard

---

[1] Cf. A. D'Abro, *The Decline of Mechanism in Modern Physics* (New York: Van Nostrand, 1939), Chap. 18; Adolf Kneser, *Das Prinzip der kleinsten Wirkung* (Leipzig: Felix Meiner, 1928); Wolfgang Yourgrau and Stanley Mandelstam, *Variational Principles in Dynamics and Quantum Theory* (London: Pitman, 1955).

It can in fact be shown that, when certain very general conditions are satisfied, all quantitative laws can be given an "extremal" formulation.

teleological notions in this sense as foreign to their task. Their dislike stems in some measure from the fear that, except when such teleological language is made rigorously precise through the use of quantitative formulations, it is apt to be misunderstood as connoting the operation of purposes.

In the second place, the physical sciences, unlike biology, are in general not concerned with a relatively special class of organized bodies, and they do not investigate the conditions making for the persistence of some selected physical system rather than of others. When a biologist ascribes a function to the kidney, he tacitly assumes that it is the kidney's contribution to the maintenance of the living animal which is under discussion; and he ignores as irrelevant to his primary interest the kidney's contribution to the maintenance of any other system of which it may also be a constituent. On the other hand, a physicist generally attempts to discuss the effects of solar radiation upon a wide variety of things; and he is reluctant to ascribe a "function" to the sun's radiation, because no one physical system of which the sun is a part is of greater interest to him than is any other such system. And similarly for the law relating the pressure and volume of a gas: if a physicist views with suspicion the formulation of this law in functional or teleological language, it is because (in addition to the reasons which have been or will be discussed) he does not regard it as his business to assign special importance, even if only by vague suggestion, to one rather than another consequence of varying pressures in a gas.

b. However, the discussion thus far can be accused, with some justice, of naïveté if not of irrelevance, on the ground that it has ignored completely the fundamental point, namely, the "goal-directed" character of organic systems. It is because living things exhibit in varying degrees adaptive and regulative structures and activities, while the systems studied in the physical sciences do not—so it is frequently claimed—that teleological explanations are peculiarly appropriate for biological systems but not for physical systems. Thus, because the solar system, or any other system of which the sun is a part, does not tend to persist in some integrated pattern of activities in the face of environmental changes, and because the constituents of the system do not undergo mutual adjustments so as to maintain this pattern in relative independence from the environment, it is preposterous to ascribe any function to the sun or to solar radiation. Nor does the fact that physics can state some of its theories in the form of extremal principles, so the objection continues, minimize the differences between biological and purely physical systems. It is true that a physical system develops in such a way as to minimize or maximize a certain magnitude which represents a property of the system as a whole. But physical systems are not organized to maintain, in the face of considerable alterations in their environment, some *par-*

ticular extremal values of such magnitudes, or to develop under widely varying conditions in the direction of realizing some particular values of such magnitudes.

Biological systems, on the other hand, do possess such organization, as a single example (which could be matched by an indefinite number of others) makes quite clear. The human body maintains many of its characteristics in a relatively steady state (or homeostasis) by complicated but coordinated physiological processes. Thus, the internal temperature of the body must remain fairly constant if it is not to be fatally injured. In point of fact, the temperature of the normal human being varies during a day only from about 97.3°F to 99.1°F, and cannot fall much below 75°F or rise much above 110°F without permanent injury to the body. However, the temperature of the external environment can fluctuate much more widely than this; and it is clear from elementary physical considerations that the body's characteristic activities would be profoundly impaired or curtailed unless it were capable of compensating for such environmental changes. But the body is indeed capable of doing just this; and in consequence its normal activities can continue, in relative independence of the temperature of the environment—provided, of course, that the environmental temperature does not fall outside a certain interval of magnitudes. The body achieves this homeostasis by means of a number of mechanisms, which serve as a series of defenses against shifts in the internal temperature. Thus, the thyroid gland is one of several that control the body's basal metabolic rate (which is the measure of the heat produced by combustion in various cells and organs); the heat radiated or conducted through the skin depends on the quantity of blood flowing through peripheral vessels, a quantity which is regulated by dilation or contraction of these vessels; sweating and the respiration rate determine the quantity of moisture that is evaporated, and so affect the internal temperature; adrenaline in the blood also stimulates internal combustion, and its secretion is affected by changes in the external temperature; and automatic muscular contractions involved in shivering are an additional source of internal heat. There are thus physiological mechanisms in the body that automatically preserve its internal temperature, despite disturbing conditions in the body's internal and external environment.[2]

Three separate questions, frequently confounded, are raised by such facts of biological organization. (1) Is it possible to formulate in general but fairly precise terms the distinguishing structure of "goal-directed" systems, but in such a way that the analysis is neutral with respect to assumptions concerning the existence of purposes or the dynamic operation of goals as instruments in their own realization? (2) Does the

---

[2] Cf. Walter B. Cannon, *The Wisdom of the Body* (New York: W. W. Norton & Company, Inc., 1932), Chap. 12.

fact, if it is a fact, that teleological explanations are customarily employed only in connection with "goal-directed" systems constitute relevant evidence for deciding the issue of whether a teleological explanation is equivalent to some nonteleological one? (3) Is it possible to explain in purely physicochemical terms—that is, exclusively in terms of the laws and theories of current physics and chemistry—the operations of biological systems? This third question will not concern us for the present, though we shall return to it later; but the other two require our immediate attention.

i. Since antiquity there have been many attempts at constructing machines and physical systems simulating the behavior of living organisms in one respect or another. None of these attempts has been entirely successful, for it has not been possible thus far to manufacture in the workshop and out of inorganic materials any device that acts fully like a living body. Nevertheless, it has been possible to construct physical systems that are self-maintaining and self-regulating in respect to certain of their features, and which therefore resemble living organisms in at least this one important characteristic. In an age in which servomechanics (governors on engines, thermostats, automatic airplane pilots, electronic calculators, radar-controlled antiaircraft firing devices, and the like) no longer excite wonder, and in which the language of cybernetics and "negative feedbacks" has become widely fashionable, the imputation of "goal-directed" behavior to purely physical systems certainly cannot be rejected as an absurdity. Whether "purposes" can also be imputed to such physical systems, as some expounders of cybernetics claim,[3] is perhaps doubtful, though the question is in large measure a semantic one; and in any event, this further issue is not relevant to the present context of discussion. Moreover, it is worth noting that the possibility of constructing self-regulating physical systems does not, by itself, constitute a proof that the activities of living organisms can be explained in exclusively physicochemical terms. Nevertheless, the fact that such systems have been constructed does suggest that there is no sharp demarcation setting off the teleological organizations, often assumed to be distinctive of living things, from the goal-directed organizations of many physical systems. At the minimum, that fact offers strong support for the presumption that the teleologically organized activities

---

[3] Cf. Arturo Rosenblueth, Norbert Wiener, Julian Bigelow, "Behavior, Purpose and Teleology," *Philosophy of Science*, Vol. X (1943), [see above, pp. 9 ff.]; Norbert Wiener, *Cybernetics* (New York: John Wiley & Sons, Inc., 1948); A. M. Turing, "Computing Machines and Intelligence," *Mind*, Vol. LIX (1950); Richard Taylor, "Comments on a Mechanistic Conception of Purposefulness," *Philosophy of Science*, Vol. XVII (1950), [see above, pp. 17 ff.], and the reply by Rosenblueth and Wiener with a rejoinder by Taylor in the same volume.

of living organisms and of their parts can be analyzed without requiring the postulation of purposes or goals as dynamic agents.

With the homeostasis of the temperature of the human body as an exemplar, let us now state in general terms the formal structure of systems possessing a goal-directed organization.[4] The characteristic feature of such systems is that they continue to manifest a certain state or property G (or that they exhibit a persistence of development "in the direction" of attaining G) in the face of a relatively extensive class of changes in their external environments or in some of their internal parts —changes which, if not compensated for by internal modification in the system, would result in the disappearance of G (or in an altered direction of development of the systems). The abstract pattern of organization of such systems can be formulated with considerable precision, although only a schematic statement of that pattern can be presented in what follows.

Let S be some system, E its external environment, and G some state, property, or mode of behavior that S possesses or is capable of possessing under suitable conditions. Assume for the moment (this assumption will eventually be relaxed) that E remains constant in all relevant respects, so that its influence upon the occurrence of G in S may be ignored. Suppose also that S is analyzable into a structure of parts or processes, such that the activities of a certain number (possibly all) of them are causally relevant for the ocurrence of G. For the sake of simplicity, assume that there are just three such parts, each capable of being in one of several distinct conditions or states. The state of each part at any given time will be represented by the predicates "A_x," "B_y," and "C_z," respectively, with numerical values of the subscripts to indicate the different particular states of the corresponding parts. Accordingly, "A_x," "B_y," and "C_z" are state variables, though they are not necessarily numerical variables, since numerical measures may not be available for representing the states of the parts; and the state of S that is causally relevant to G at any given time will thus be expressed by a specialization of the matrix "$(A_x B_y C_z)$." The state variables may, however, be quite complex in form—for example, "A_x" may represent the state of the peripheral blood vessels in a human body at a given time— and they may be either individual or statistical coordinates. But in order to avoid inessential complications in exposition, we shall suppose that,

---

[4] The following discussion is heavily indebted to G. Sommerhoff, *Analytical Biology* (London: Oxford University Press, 1950). Cf. also Alfred J. Lotka, *Elements of Physical Biology* (Baltimore: Williams and Wilkins Co., 1925), Chap. 25; W. Ross Ashby, *Design for a Brain* (London: Chapman and Hall, Ltd., 1953), and *An Introduction to Cybernetics* (New York: J. Wiley, 1952, 1956); and R. B. Braithwaite, *Scientific Explanation* (London: University of Cambridge Press, 1954), Chap. 10. [See above, pp. 27 ff.]

whatever the nature of the state variables, in respect to the states they represent S is a deterministic system: the states of S change in such a way that, if S is in the same state at any two different moments, the corresponding states of S after equal lapses of time from those moments will also be the same.

One further important general assumption must also be made explicit. Each of the state variables can be assigned any particular "value" to characterize a state, provided the value is compatible with the known character of the part of S whose state the variable represents. In effect, therefore, the values of "A_x" must fall into a certain restricted class K_A; and there are similar classes K_B and K_C for the permissible values of the other two state variables. The reason for these restrictions will be clear from an example. If S is the human body, and "A_x" states the degree of dilation of peripheral blood vessels, it is obvious that this degree cannot exceed some maximum value; for it would be absurd to suppose that the blood vessels might have a mean diameter of, say, five feet. On the other hand, the possible values of one state variable *at a given time* will be assumed to be independent of the possible values of the other state variables *at that time*. This assumption must not be misunderstood. It does not assert that the value of a variable at one time is independent of the values of the other variables at some *other* time; it merely stipulates that the value of a variable at some specified instant is not a function of the values of the other variables *at that very same instant*. The assumption is the one normally made for state variables, and is introduced in part to avoid redundant coordinates of state. For example, the state variables in classical mechanics are the position and the momentum coordinates of a particle at an instant. Although the position of a particle at one instant will in general depend on its momentum (and position) at some *previous* time, the position at a given instant is not a function of the momentum *at that given instant*. If the position were such a function of the momentum, it is clear that the state of a particle in classical mechanics could be specified by just one state variable (the momentum), so that mention of the position would be redundant. In our present discussion we are similarly assuming that none of the state variables is dispensable, so that any combination of simultaneous values of the state variables yields a permissible specialization of the matrix "$(A_x B_y C_z)$," provided that the values of the variables belong to the classes K_A, K_B, and K_C, respectively. This is tantamount to saying that, apart from the proviso, the state of S stipulated to be causally relevant to G must be so analyzed that the state variables employed for describing the state at a given time are mutually independent of one another.

Suppose now that if S is in the state $(A_0 B_0 C_0)$ at some initial time, then either S has the property G, or else a sequence of changes occurs in S as a consequence of which S will possess G at some subsequent time. Let us call such an initial state of S a "causally effective state with respect to G," or a "G-state" for short. Not every possible state of S need be a G-state, for one of the causally relevant parts of S may be in a certain state at a given time, such that *no* combination of possible states of the other parts will yield a G-state for S. Thus, suppose that S is the human body, G the property of having an internal temperature lying in the range 97° to 99°F, A_x again the state of the peripheral blood vessels, B_y the state of the thyroid glands, and C_z the state of the adrenal glands. It may happen that B_y assumes a value (for example, corresponding to acute hyperactivity) such that for no possible values of A_x and C_z, respectively, will G be realized. It is of course also conceivable that no possible state of S is a G-state, so that in fact G is never realized in S. For example, if S is the human body and G the property of having an internal temperature lying in the range from 150° to 160°, then there is no G-state for S. On the other hand, more than one possible state of S may be a G-state. But if there is more than one possible G-state, then (since S has been assumed to be a deterministic system) the one that is realized at a given time is uniquely determined by the actual state of S at some previous time. The case in which there is more than one such possible G-state for S is of particular relevance to the present discussion, and we must now consider it more closely.

Assume once more that at some initial time t_0, the system S is in the G-state $(A_0B_0C_0)$. Suppose, however, that a change occurs in S so that in consequence A_0 is caused to vary, with the result that at time t_1 subsequent to t_0 the state variable "A_x" has some other value. What value it will have at t_1 will in general depend on the particular changes that have taken place in S. We shall assume, however, that S will continue to be in a G-state at time t_1, provided that the values of "A_x" at t_1 fall into a certain class K_A' (a subclass of K_A) containing more than one member, and provided also that certain further changes take place in the other state variables. To fix our ideas, suppose that A_1 and A_2 are the only possible members of K_A'; and assume also that neither $(A_1B_0C_0)$ nor $(A_2B_0C_0)$ is a G-state. In other words, if A_0 were changed into A_3 (a member of K_A but not of K_A'), S would no longer be in a G-state; but even though the new value of "A_x" falls into K_A', if this were the only change in S the system would also no longer be in a G-state at time t_1. Let us assume, however, S to be so constituted that if A_0 is caused to vary so that the value of "A_x" at time t_1 falls into K_A', there will be further compensatory changes in the values of some or all of the other state variables such that S continues to be in a G-state.

These further changes are stipulated to be of the following kind. If, as a concomitant of the change in A_0, the values of "B_y" and "C_z" at time t_1 fall into certain classes K_B' and K_C', respectively (where of course K_B' is a subclass, though not necessarily a proper subclass, of K_B, and K_C' is a subclass of K_C), then for each value in K_A' there is a unique pair of values, one member of the pair belonging to K_B' and the other to K_C', such that for those values S continues to be in a G-state at time t_1. These pairs of values can be taken to be elements in a certain class K_{BC}'. On the other hand, were the altered values of "B_y" and "C_z" not accompanied by the indicated changes in the value of "A_x," the system S would no longer be in a G-state at time t_1. In terms of the notation just introduced, accordingly, if at time t_1 the state variables of S have values such that two of them are members of a pair belonging to the class K_{BC}' while the value of the third variable is not the corresponding element in K_A', then S is not in a G-state. For example, suppose that, when A_0 changes into A_1, the initial G-state $(A_0B_0C_0)$ is changed into the G-state $(A_1B_1C_1)$, but that $(A_0B_1C_1)$ is not a G-state; and suppose also that when A_0 changes into A_2, the initial G-state is changed into the G-state $(A_2B_1C_2)$, with $(A_0B_1C_2)$ not a G-state. In this example, K_A' is the class (A_1, A_2); K_B' is the class (B_1); K_C' is the class (C_1, C_2); and K_{BC}' is the class of pairs $[(B_1, C_1), (B_1, C_2)]$, with A_1 corresponding to the pair (B_1, C_1) and A_2 to the pair (B_1, C_2).

Let us now bring together these various points, and introduce some definitions. Assume S to be a system satisfying the following conditions: (1) S can be analyzed into a set of related parts or processes, a certain number of which (say three, namely A, B, and C) are causally relevant to the occurrence in S of some property or mode of behavior G. At any time the state of S causally relevant to G can be specified by assigning values to a set of state variables "A_x," "B_y," and "C_z." The values of the state variables for any given time can be assigned independently of one another; but the possible values of each variable are restricted, in virtue of the nature of S, to certain classes of values K_A, K_B, and K_C, respectively. (2) If S is in a G-state at a given initial instant t_0 falling into some interval of time T, a change in any of the state variables will in general take S out of the G-state. Assume that a change is initiated in one of the state variables (say the parameter "A"); and suppose that in fact the possible values of the parameter at time t_1 within the interval T but later than t_0 fall into a certain class K_A', with the proviso that if this were the sole change in the state of S the system would be taken out of its G-state. Let us call this initiating change a "primary variation" in S. (3) However, the parts A, B, and C of S are so related that, when the primary variation in S occurs, the remaining parameters also vary, and in point of fact their values at time t_1 fall into certain classes K_B' and K_C', respectively. These changes induced in B and C thus yield unique pairs of values for their parameters at time t_1, the pairs being elements of a class K_{BC}'. Were these latter changes the only ones in the initial G-state of S, unaccompanied by the indicated primary variation in S, the system would not be in a G-state at time t_1. (4) As a matter of fact, however, the elements of K_A' and K_{BC}' correspond to each other in a uniquely reciprocal manner, such that, when S is in a state specified by these corresponding values of the state variables, the system is in a G-state at time t_1. Let us call the changes in the state of S induced by the primary variation and represented by the pairs of values in K_{BC}' the "adaptive variations" of S with respect to the primary variation of S (that is, with respect to possible values of the parameter "A" in K_A'). Finally, when a system S satisfies all these assumptions for every pair of initial and subsequent instants in the interval T, the parts of S causally relevant to G will be said to be "directively organized during the interval of time T with respect to G" —or, more shortly, to be "directively organized," if the reference to G and T can be taken for granted.

This discussion of directively organized systems has been based on several simplifying assumptions. However, the analysis can be readily generalized for a system requiring the use of any number of state variables (including numerical ones), for changes in the state of a system that are initiated in more than one of the causally relevant parts of the system, and for continuous as well as discrete series of transitions from one G-state of a system to another.[5] Indeed, it is not difficult to develop

---

[5] When the state coordinates are assumed to be numerical, it is possible to formulate the conditions for a directively organized system as follows:

Let S be a system, G a trait of S, and "x_1," "x_2," . . . , "x_n" the state variables for G. The variables are stipulated to be independent and continuous functions of the time; and superscripts will indicate their values at any given time t.

a) If S is a deterministic system with respect to G, the state of S at time t is uniquely determined by the state of S at some preceding time t_0. Hence

$$x_1{}^t = f_1(x_1{}^{t_0}, \ldots, x_n{}^{t_0}, t - t_0)$$
$$\cdots\cdots\cdots\cdots\cdots\cdots\cdots\cdots\cdots$$
$$x_i{}^t = f_i(x_1{}^{t_0}, \ldots, x_n{}^{t_0}, t - t_0)$$
$$\cdots\cdots\cdots\cdots\cdots\cdots\cdots\cdots\cdots$$
$$x_n{}^t = f_n(x_1{}^{t_0}, \ldots, x_n{}^{t_0}, t - t_0)$$

where the f_i's are single-valued functions of their arguments. Their first derivates with respect to the time are also single-valued functions of their arguments and of no other functions of the time.

b) Since the special character of S imposes restrictions on the values of the within this framework of analysis the notion of a system exhibiting self-regulatory behaviors with respect to several G's at the same time, alternative (and even incompatible) G's at different times, a set of G's constituting a hierarchy on the basis of some postulated scale of "relative importance," or more generally a set of G's whose membership changes with time and circumstance. But apart from complexity, nothing im-

state variable, the values of each variable "x_i" will fall within an interval determined by a pair of numbers a_i and b_i. That is,

$$a_i \leq x_i \leq b_i$$

with $i \leq 1, 2, \ldots, n$, or alternately

$$x_i \, \epsilon \, \Delta x_i$$

where Δx_i is some definite interval and "ϵ" is the usual sign for class membership.

c) If S is in a G-state at a given time t falling into a given period of time T, the state variable must satisfy a set of conditions or equations. That S is in a G-state at time t can be expressed by requirement:

$$g_1(x_1^t, \ldots, x_n^t) = 0$$
$$\cdots\cdots\cdots\cdots\cdots$$
$$g_r(x_1^t, \ldots, x_n^t) = 0$$

where each g_j $(j = 1, 2, \ldots, r)$ is a function differentiable with respect to each of the state variables, and $r < n$.

d) The values of each state variable "x_i^t" satisfying these equations defining a G-state of S fall into certain restricted intervals:

$$a_i \leq a_i^G \leq x_i^t \leq b_i^G \leq b_i$$

or alternately:

$$x_i^t \, \epsilon \, \Delta x_i^G$$

where Δx_i^G falls into the interval Δx_i.

e) Assume that S is in a G-state at the initial time t_0 during the period T, and that a change takes place in the value of some state variable "x_k" so that at time t later than t_0 in T its value is x_k^t. The condition that this change is a G-preserving change (so that $x_k^t \, \epsilon \, \Delta x_k^G$), is that for each function g_j:

$$\frac{\partial g_j}{\partial x_k^{t_0}} = \frac{\partial g_j}{\partial x_1^t}\frac{\partial x_1^t}{\partial x_k^{t_0}} + \frac{\partial g_j}{\partial x_2^t}\frac{\partial x_2^t}{\partial x_k^{t_0}} + \cdots + \frac{\partial g_j}{\partial x_n^t}\frac{\partial x_n^t}{\partial x_k^{t_0}} = 0$$

f) The system S is directively organized with respect to G during T if, when such G-preserving changes occur in any given state variable "x_k," there are compensating variations in one or more of the other state variables. Accordingly, there must be at least one function g_j such that in the partial differential equations just mentioned there are at least two nonvanishing summands. That is, there are at least two summands in one or more of these equations such that

$$\frac{\partial g_j}{\partial x_i^t}\frac{\partial x_i^t}{\partial x_k^{t_0}} \neq 0$$

mediately relevant would be gained by such extensions of the analysis; and the schematic and incompletely general definitions that have been presented will suffice for our purposes.

It will in any case be clear from the above account that if S is directively organized, the persistence of G is in an important sense independent of the variations in any one of the causally relevant parts of S, provided that these variations do not exceed certain limits. For although by hypothesis the occurrence of G in S depends upon S being in a G-state, and therefore upon the state of the causally relevant parts of S, an alteration in the state of one of those parts may be compensated by induced changes in one or more of the other causally relevant parts, so as to preserve S in its assumed G-state. The *prima facie* distinctive character of so-called "goal-directed" or teleological systems is thus formulated by the stated conditions for a directively organized system. The above analysis has therefore shown that the notion of a teleological system can be explicated in a manner not requiring the adoption of teleology as a fundamental or unanalyzable category. What may be called the "degree of directive organization" of a system, or perhaps the "degree of persistence" of some trait of a system, can also be made explicit in terms of the above analysis. For the property G is maintained in S (or S persists in its development, which eventuates in G) to the extent that the range K_A' of the possible primary variations is associated with the range of induced compensatory changes K_{BC}' (that is, the adaptive variations) such that S is preserved in its G-state. The more inclusive the range K_A' that is associated with such compensatory changes, the more is the persistence of G independent of variations in the state of S. Accordingly, on the assumption that it is possible to specify a measure for the range K_A', the "degree of directive organization" of S with respect to variations in the state parameter "A" could be defined as the measure of this range.

We may now relax the assumption that the external environment E has no influence upon S. But in dropping this assumption, we merely complicate the analysis, without introducing anything novel into it. For suppose that there is some factor in E which is causally relevant to the occurrence of G in S, and whose state at any time can be specified by some determinate form of the state variable "F_w." Then the state of the enlarged system S' (consisting of S together with E) which is causally relevant to the occurrence of G in S is specified by some determinate form of the matrix "$(A_x B_y C_z F_w)$," and the discussion proceeds as before. However, it is generally not the case that a variation in any of the internal parts of S produces any significant variation in the environmental factors. What usually is the case is that the environmental factors vary quite independently of the internal parts; they do not undergo changes which compensate for changes in the state of S; and, while a limited range of changes in them may be compensated by changes in S so as to preserve S in some G-state, most of the states which environmental factors are capable of assuming cannot be so compensated by changes in S. It is customary, therefore, to talk of the "degree of plasticity" or the "degree of adaptability" of organic systems in relation to their environments, and not conversely. However, it is possible to define these notions without special reference to organic systems, in a manner analogous to the definition of the "degree of directive organization" of a system already suggested. Thus, suppose that the variations in the environmental state variable "F," assumed to be compensated by further changes in S so as to preserve S in some G-state, all fall into the class K_F'. If an appropriate measure for the magnitude of this class could be devised, the "degree of plasticity" of S with respect to the maintenance of some G in relation to F could then be defined as equal to the measure of K_F'.

This must suffice as an outline of the abstract structure of goal-directed or teleological systems. The account given deliberately leaves undiscussed the detailed mechanisms involved in the operation of particular teleological systems; and it simply assumes that all such systems can in principle be analyzed into parts which are causally relevant to the maintenance of some feature in those systems, and which stand to each other and to environmental factors in determinate relations capable of being formulated as general laws. The discovery and analysis of such detailed mechanisms is the task of specialized scientific inquiry. Accordingly, since the above account deals only with what is assumed to be the common distinctive structure of teleological systems, it is also entirely neutral on such substantive issues as to whether the operations of all teleological systems can be explained in exclusively physicochemical terms. On the other hand, if the account is at least approximately adequate, it requires a positive answer to the question whether the distinguishing features of goal-directed systems can be formulated without invoking purposes and goals as dynamic agents.

There is, however, one further matter that must be briefly discussed. The definition of directively organized systems has been so stated that it can be used to characterize both biological and nonvital systems. It is in fact easy to cite illustrations for the definition from either domain. The human body with respect to homeostasis of its internal temperature is an example from biology; a building equipped with a furnace and thermostat is an example from physicochemistry. Nevertheless, although the definition is not intended to distinguish between vital and nonvital teleological systems—for the differences between such systems must be stated in terms of the specific material composition, characteristics, and activities they manifest—it *is* intended to set off systems having a *prima facie* "goal-directed" character from systems usually not so characterized. The question therefore remains whether the definition does achieve this aim, or whether on the contrary it is so inclusive that almost *any* system (whether it is ordinarily judged to be goal-directed or not) satisfies it.

Now there are certainly many physicochemical systems that are not ordinarily regarded as being "goal-directed" but that nevertheless appear to conform to the definition of directively organized systems proposed above. Thus, a pendulum at rest, an elastic solid, a steady electric current flowing through a conductor, a chemical system in thermodynamic equilibrium, are obvious examples of such systems. It seems therefore that the definition of directive organization—and in consequence the proposed analysis of "goal-directed" or "teleological" systems—fails to attain its intended objective. However, two comments are in order on the point of issue. In the first place, though we admittedly do distinguish between systems that are goal-directed and those which are not, the distinction is highly vague, and there are many systems which cannot be classified definitely as of one kind rather than another. Thus, is the child's toy sometimes known as the "walking beetle"—which turns aside when it reaches the edge of a table and fails to fall off, because an idle wheel is then brought into play through the action of an "antenna"—a goal-directed system or not? Is a virus such a system? Is the system consisting of members of some biological species that has undergone evolutionary development in a steady direction (for example, the development of gigantic antlers in the male Irish elk), a goal-directed one? Moreover, some systems have been classified as "teleological" at one time and in relation to one body of knowledge, only to be reclassified as "nonteleological" at a later time, as knowledge concerning the physics of mechanisms improved. "Nature does nothing in vain" was a maxim commonly accepted in pre-Newtonian physics, and on the basis of the doctrine of "natural places" even the descent of bodies and the ascent of smoke were regarded as goal-directed. Accordingly, it is at least an open question whether the current distinction between systems that are goal-directed and those that are not invariably has an identifiable objective basis (that is, in terms of differences between the actual organizations of such systems), and whether the *same* system may not often be classified in alternative ways depending on the perspective from which it is viewed and on the antecedent assumptions adopted for analyzing its structure.

In the second place, it is by no means certain that physical systems such as the pendulum at rest, which is not usually regarded as goal-directed, really do conform to the definition of "directively organized" systems proposed above. Consider a simple pendulum that is initially at rest and is then given a small impulse (say by a sudden gust of wind);

and assume that apart from the constraints of the system and the force of gravitation the only force that acts on the bob is the friction of the air. Then on the usual physical assumptions, the pendulum will perform harmonic oscillations with decreasing amplitudes, and finally assume its initial position of rest. The system here consists of the pendulum and the various forces acting on it, while the property G is the state of the pendulum when it is at rest at the lowest point of its path of oscillation. By hypothesis, its length and the mass of the bob are fixed, and so is the force of gravitation acting on it, as well as the coefficient of damping; the variables are the impulsive force of the gust of wind, and the restoring force which operates on the bob as a consequence of the constraints of the system and of the presence of the gravitational field. However—and this is the crucial point—these two forces are *not* independent of one another. Thus, if the effective component of the former has a certain magnitude, the restoring force will have an equal magnitude with an opposite direction. Accordingly, if the state of the system at a given time were specified in terms of state variables which take these forces as values, these state variables would not satisfy one of the stipulated conditions for state variables of directively organized systems; for the value of one of them at a given time is uniquely determined by the value of the other at that same time. In short, the values of these proposed state variables at any given instant are not independent.[6] It there-

---

[6] This can be shown in greater detail by considering the usual mathematical discussion of the simple pendulum. If l is the length of the pendulum, m the mass of its bob, g the constant force of gravity, k the coefficient of damping due to air resistance, t the time as measured from some fixed instant, and s the distance of the bob along its path of oscillation from the point of initial rest, the differential equation of motion of the pendulum (on the assumption that the amplitude of vibration is small) is

$$m\frac{d^2s}{dt^2} + k\frac{ds}{dt} + \frac{mg}{l}s = 0$$

If at time t_0 the pendulum is at rest, both s_0 and $v_0 \left[= \left(\frac{ds}{dt}\right)_0 \right]$ are zero, so that

$$\left(m\frac{d^2s}{dt^2} \right)_0 = 0;$$

that is, no unbalanced forces are acting on the bob. Suppose now that at time t_1 the bob is at s_1 with a velocity v_1; the restoring force will then be

$$\left(m\frac{d^2t}{dt^2} \right)_1 = -kv_1 - \frac{mg}{l}s_1$$

But an impulsive force F_1 communicated to the bob at time t_1 uniquely determines the velocity v_1 and the position s_1 of the bob at that time. Hence the restoring force can be calculated, so that it is uniquely determined by the impulsive force.

fore follows that the simple pendulum is not a directively organized system in the sense of the definition presented. Moreover, it is also possible to show in a similar manner that a number of other systems, generally regarded as nonteleological ones, fail to satisfy that definition. Whether one could show this for all systems currently so regarded is admittedly an open question. However, since there are at least some systems not usually characterized as teleological which must also be so characterized on the basis of the definition, the label of "directively organized system" whose meaning the definition explicates does not apply to everything whatsoever, and it does not baptize a distinction without a difference. There are therefore some grounds for claiming that the definition achieves what it was designed to achieve, and that it formulates the abstract structure commonly held to be distinctive of "goal-directed" systems.

ii. We can now settle quite briefly the second question, on page 72, we undertook to examine, namely, whether the fact that teleological explanations are usually advanced only in connection with "goal-directed" systems affects the claim that, in respect to its asserted content, every teleological explanation is translatable into an equivalent nonteleological one. The answer is clearly in the negative, if such systems are analyzable as directively organized ones in the sense of the above definition. For on the supposition that the notion of a goal-directed system can be explicated in the proposed manner, the characteristics that ostensibly distinguish such systems from those not goal-directed can be formulated entirely in nonteleological language. In consequence, every statement about the subject matter of a teleological explanation can in principle be rendered in nonteleological language, so that such explanations together with all assertions about the contexts of their use are translatable into logically equivalent nonteleological formulations.

Why, then, does it seem odd to render physical statements such as Boyle's law in teleological form? The answer is plain, if indeed teleological statements (and in particular, teleological explanations) are normally advanced only in connection with subject matters that are assumed to be directively organized. The oddity does not stem from any difference between the explicitly asserted content of a physical law and of its purported teleologically formulated equivalent. A teleological version of Boyle's law appears strange and unacceptable because such a formulation would usually be construed as resting on the assumption that a gas enclosed in a volume is a directively organized system, in contradiction to the normally accepted assumption that a volume of gas is not such a system. In a sense, therefore, a teleological explanation does connote more than does its *prima facie* equivalent nonteleological translation. For the former presupposes, while the latter normally does not, that the system under consideration in the explanation is directively organized. Nevertheless, if the above analysis is generally sound, this "surplus meaning" of teleological statements can always be expressed in nonteleological language.

THE LOGIC OF
FUNCTIONAL ANALYSIS

CARL G. HEMPEL

Empirical science, in all its major branches, seeks not only to *describe* the phenomena in the world of our experience, but also to *explain* or *understand* their occurrence: it is concerned not just with the "what?", "when?", and "where?", but definitely, and often predominantly, with the "why?" of the phenomena it investigates.

That explanation and understanding constitute a common objective of the various scientific disciplines is widely recognized today. However, it is often held that there exist fundamental differences between the explanatory *methods* appropriate to the different fields of empirical science, and especially between those of the "exact" natural sciences and those required for an adequate understanding of the behavior of humans or other organisms, taken individually or in groups. In the exact natural sciences, according to this view, all explanation is achieved ultimately by reference to causal or correlational antecedents; whereas in psychology and the social and historical disciplines—and, according to some,

Pp. 271-287 "The Logic of Functional Analysis" by C. G. Hempel in *Symposium on Sociological Theory,* edited by Llewellyn Gross. Copyright © 1959 by Harper & Row, Publishers, Incorporated. Reprinted with their permission.

even in biology—the establishment of causal or correlational connections, while desirable and important, is not sufficient. Proper understanding of the phenomena studied in these fields is held to require other types of explanation.

Perhaps the most important of the alternative methods that have been developed for this purpose is the method of functional analysis, which has found extensive use in biology, psychology, sociology, and anthropology. This procedure raises problems of considerable interest for the comparative methodology of empirical science. This essay is an attempt to clarify some of these problems; its object is to examine the logical structure of functional analysis and its explanatory and predictive significance by means of an explicit confrontation with the principal characteristics of the explanatory procedures used in the physical sciences. We begin by a brief examination of the latter.

1. NOMOLOGICAL EXPLANATION: DEDUCTIVE AND INDUCTIVE

In a beaker filled to the brim with water at room temperature, there floats a chunk of ice which partly extends above the surface. As the ice gradually melts, one might expect the water in the beaker to overflow. Actually, however, the water level remains unchanged. How is this to be explained? The key to an answer is provided by Archimedes' principle, according to which a solid body floating in a liquid displaces a volume of liquid which has the same weight as the body itself. Hence the chunk of ice has the same weight as the volume of water its submerged portion displaces. Now, since melting does not affect the weights involved, the water into which the ice turns has the same weight as the ice itself, and hence, the same weight as the water initially displaced by the submerged portion of the ice. Having the same weight, it also has the same volume as the displaced water; hence the melting ice yields a volume of water that suffices exactly to fill the space initially occupied by the submerged part of the ice. Therefore, the water level remains unchanged.

This account (which deliberately disregards certain effects of small magnitude) is an example of an argument intended to explain a certain event. Like any explanatory argument, it falls into two parts, which will be called the *explanans* and the *explanandum*.[1] The latter is the state-

---

[1] These terms are given preference over the more familiar words "explicans" and "explicandum," in order to reserve the latter for use in the context of philosophical explication in the technical sense proposed by R. Carnap; see, for example, his *Logical Foundations of Probability* (Chicago: University of Chicago Press, 1950), secs. 1-3. The terms "explanans" and "explanandum" were introduced, for this reason, in an earlier article: Carl G. Hempel and P.

ment, or set of statements, describing the phenomenon to be explained; the former is the statement, or set of statements, adduced to provide an explanation. In our illustration, the explanandum states that at the end of the process, the beaker contains only water, with its surface at the same level as at the beginning. To explain this, the explanans adduces, first of all, certain laws of physics; among them, Archimedes' principle; laws to the effect that at temperatures above 0°C. and atmospheric pressure, a body of ice turns into a body of water having the same weight; and the law that, at any fixed temperature and pressure, amounts of water that are equal in weight are also equal in volume.

In addition to these laws, the explanans contains a second group of statements; these describe certain particular circumstances which, in the experiment, precede the outcome to be explained; such as the facts that at the beginning, there is a chunk of ice floating in a beaker filled with water; that the water is at room temperature; and that the beaker is surrounded by air at the same temperature and remains undisturbed until the end of the experiment.

The explanatory import of the whole argument lies in showing that the outcome described in the explanandum was to be expected in view of the antecedent circumstances and the general laws listed in the explanans. More precisely, the explanation may be construed as an argument in which the explanandum is deduced from the explanans. Our example then illustrates what we will call explanation by deductive subsumption under general laws, or briefly, *deductive nomological explanation*. The general form of such an explanation is given by the following schema:

$$(2.1) \qquad \frac{\begin{matrix} L_1, L_2, \ldots, L_m \\ C_1, C_2, \ldots, C_n \end{matrix}}{E} \qquad \begin{matrix} \text{Explanans} \\ \\ \text{Explanandum} \end{matrix}$$

Here, $L_1, L_2, \ldots, L_m$ are general laws and $C_1, C_2, \ldots, C_n$ are statements of particular fact; the horizontal line separating the conclusion E from the premises indicates that the former follows logically from the latter.

―――――――――

Oppenheim, "Studies in the Logic of Explanation," *Philosophy of Science*, Vol. XV (1948), 135-75. Reprinted in part in H. Feigl and M. Brodbeck, eds., *Readings in the Philosophy of Science* (New York: Appleton-Century-Crofts, Inc., 1953). While that article does not deal explicitly with inductive explanation, its first four sections contain various further considerations on deductive explanation that are relevant to the present study. For a careful critical examination of some points of detail discussed in the earlier article, such as especially the relation between explanation and prediction, see the essay by I. Scheffler, "Explanation, Prediction, and Abstraction," *The British Journal for the Philosophy of Science*, Vol. VII (1957), 293-309, which also contains some interesting comments bearing on functional analysis.

In our example, the phenomenon to be explained is a particular event that takes place at a certain place and time. But the method of deductive subsumption under general laws lends itself also to the explanation of what might be called "general facts" or uniformities, such as those expressed in laws of nature. For example, the question why Galileo's law holds for physical bodies falling freely near the earth's surface can be answered by showing that that law refers to a special case of accelerated motion under gravitational attraction, and that it can be deduced from the general laws for such motion (namely, Newton's laws of motion and of gravitation) by applying these to the special case where two bodies are involved, one of them the earth and the other the falling object, and where the distance between their centers of gravity equals the length of the earth's radius. Thus, an explanation of the regularities expressed by Galileo's law can be achieved by deducing the latter from the Newtonian laws and from statements specifying the mass and the radius of the earth; the latter two yield the value of the constant acceleration of free fall near the earth.

It might be helpful to mention one further illustration of the role of deductive nomological explanation in accounting for particular facts as well as for general uniformities or laws. The occurrence of a rainbow on a given occasion can be deductively explained by reference to (1) certain particular determining conditions, such as the presence of raindrops in the air, sunlight falling on these drops, the observer facing away from the sun, and so forth, and (2) certain general laws, especially those of optical reflection, refraction, and dispersion. The fact that these laws hold can be explained in turn by deduction from the more comprehensive principles of, say, the electromagnetic theory of light.

Thus, the method of deductive nomological explanation accounts for a particular event by subsuming it under general laws in the manner represented by the schema (2.1); and it can similarly serve to explain the fact that a given law holds by showing that the latter is subsumable, in the same fashion, under more comprehensive laws or theoretical principles. In fact, one of the main objectives of a theory (such as, say, the electromagnetic theory of light) is precisely to provide a set of principles —often expressed in terms of "hypothetical," not directly observable, entities (such as electric and magnetic field vectors)—which will deductively account for a group of antecedently established "empirical generalizations" (such as the laws of rectilinear propagation, reflection, and refraction of light). Frequently, a theoretical explanation will show that the empirical generalizations hold only approximately. For example, the application of Newtonian theory to free fall near the earth yields a law that is like Galileo's except that the acceleration of the fall is seen not to be strictly constant, but to vary slightly with geographical location, altitude above sea level, and certain other factors.

The general laws or theoretical principles that serve to account for empirical generalizations may in turn be deductively subsumable under even more comprehensive principles; for example, Newton's theory of gravitation can be subsumed, as an approximation, under that of the general theory of relativity. Obviously, this explanatory hierarchy has to end at some point. Thus, at any time in the development of empirical science, there will be certain facts which, at that time, are not explainable; these include the most comprehensive general laws and theoretical principles then known and, of course, many empirical generalizations and particular facts for which no explanatory principles are available at the time. But this does not imply that certain facts are intrinsically unexplainable and thus must remain unexplained forever: any particular fact as yet unexplainable, and any general principle, however comprehensive, may subsequently be found to be explainable by subsumption under even more inclusive principles.

Causal explanation is a special type of deductive nomological explanation; for a certain event or set of events can be said to have caused a specified "effect" only if there are general laws connecting the former with the latter in such a way that, given a description of the antecedent events, the occurrence of the effect can be deduced with the help of the laws. For example, the explanation of the lengthening of a given iron bar as having been caused by an increase in its temperature amounts to an argument of the form (2.1) whose explanans includes (a) statements specifying the initial length of the bar and indicating that the bar is made of iron and that its temperature was raised, (b) a law to the effect that the length of any iron bar increases with the temperature.[2]

Not every deductive nomological explanation is a causal explanation, however. We cannot properly say, for example, that the regularities expressed by Newton's laws of motion and of gravitation *cause* the free fall of bodies near the earth's surface to satisfy Galileo's laws.

Now we must give at least brief consideration to another type of explanation, which again accounts for a given phenomenon by reference to general laws, but in a manner which does not fit the deductive pattern (2.1). For example, when little Henry catches the mumps, this might be explained by pointing out that he contracted the disease from a friend

---

[2] An explanation by means of laws which are causal in the technical sense of theoretical physics also has the form (2.1) of a deductive nomological explanation. In this case, the laws invoked must meet certain conditions as to mathematical form, and $C_1, C_2, \ldots, C_n$ express so-called boundary conditions. For a fuller account of the concepts of causal law and of causality as understood in theoretical physics, see, for example, H. Margenau, *The Nature of Physical Reality* (New York: McGraw-Hill Book Company, Inc., 1950), Chap. 19; or Ph. Frank, *Philosophy of Science* (Englewood Cliffs, N.J.: Prentice-Hall, Inc., 1957), Chaps. 11, 12.

with whom he played for several hours just a day before the latter was confined with a severe case of mumps. The particular antecedent factors involved in this argument are Henry's exposure and, let us assume, the fact that Henry had not had the mumps before. But to connect these with the event to be explained, we cannot invoke a general law to the effect that under the conditions just mentioned, the exposed person invariably contracts the mumps: what can be asserted is only a high statistical probability that the disease will be transmitted. Again, when a neurotic trait in an adult is psychoanalytically explained by reference to critical childhood experiences, the argument explicitly or implicitly claims that the case at hand is but an exemplification of certain general laws governing the development of neuroses. But, surely, whatever specific laws of this kind might be adduced at present can purport, at the very best, to express probabilistic trends rather than deterministic uniformities: they may be construed as *laws of statistical form,* or briefly as *statistical laws,* to the effect that, given the childhood experiences in question—plus, presumably, certain particular environmental conditions in later life—there is such and such a statistical probability that a specified kind of neurosis will develop. Such statistical laws differ in form from strictly universal laws of the kind adduced in our earlier examples of explanatory arguments. In the simplest case, a *law of strictly universal form,* or briefly, a *universal law,* is a statement to the effect that in *all* cases satisfying certain antecedent conditions A (for example, heating of a gas under constant pressure), an event of a specified kind B (for example, an increase in the volume of the gas) will occur; whereas a law of statistical form asserts that the probability for conditions A to be accompanied by an event of kind B has some specific value p.

Explanatory arguments which, in the manner just illustrated, account for a phenomenon by reference to statistical laws are not of the strictly deductive type (2.1). For example, the explanans consisting of information about Henry's exposure to the mumps and of a statistical law about the transmission of this disease does not logically imply the conclusion that Henry catches the mumps; it does not make that conclusion necessary, but, as we might say, more or less probable, depending upon the probability specified by the statistical laws. An argument of this kind, then, accounts for a phenomenon by showing that its occurrence is highly probable in view of certain particular facts and statistical laws specified in the explanans. An account of this type will be called an *explanation by inductive subsumption under statistical laws,* or briefly, an *inductive explanation.* For the purposes of the present essay, this sketchy characterization of the explanatory use of statistical laws will suffice; a precise analysis of the method, which requires an inquiry into rather complex technical issues in inductive logic and the theory of statistical inference, reveals certain fundamental differences between deductive and inductive explanation.[3]

The two types of explanation we have distinguished will both be said to be forms of *nomological explanation;* for either of them accounts for a given phenomenon by "subsuming it under laws," that is, by showing that its occurrence could have been inferred—either deductively or with a high probability—by applying certain laws of universal or of statistical form to specified antecedent circumstances. Thus, a nomological explanation shows that we might in fact have *predicted* the phenomenon at hand, either deductively or with a high probability, if, at an earlier time, we had taken cognizance of the facts stated in the explanans.

But the predictive power of a nomological explanation goes much farther than this: precisely because its explanans contains general laws, it permits predictions concerning occurrences other than that referred to in the explanandum. These predictions provide a means of testing the empirical soundness of the explanans. For example, the laws invoked in a deductive explanation of the form (2.1) imply that the kind of event described in E will recur whenever and wherever circumstances of the kind described by C_1, C_2, . . . , C_n are realized; for example, when the experiment with ice floating in water is repeated, the outcome will be the same. In addition, the laws will yield predictions as to what is going to happen under certain specifiable conditions which differ from those mentioned in C_1, C_2, . . . , C_n. For example, the laws invoked in our illustration also yield the prediction that if a chunk of ice were floating in a beaker filled to the brim with concentrated brine, which has a greater specific gravity than water, some of the liquid would overflow as the ice was melting. Again, the Newtonian laws of motion and of gravitation, which may be used to explain various aspects of planetary motion, have predictive consequences for a variety of totally different phenomena, such as free fall near the earth, the motion of a pendulum, the tides, and many others.

This kind of account of further phenomena which is made possible by a nomological explanation is not limited to future events, but may refer to the past as well. For example, given certain information about the present locations and velocities of the celestial bodies involved, the principles of Newtonian mechanics and of optics yield not only predic-

---

[3] Some brief but lucid and stimulating comments on explanation by means of statistical laws will be found in S. E. Gluck, "Do Statistical Laws Have Explanatory Efficacy?" *Philosophy of Science,* Vol. XXII (1955), 34-38. For a much fuller analysis of the logic of statistical inference, see R. B. Braithwaite, *Scientific Explanation* (London: Cambridge University Press, 1953), Chaps. 5, 6, 7. For a study of the logic of inductive inference in general, Carnap's *Logical Foundations of Probability, op. cit.,* is of great importance.

tions about future solar and lunar eclipses, but also "postdictions," or "retrodictions," about past ones. Analogously, the statistical laws of radioactive decay, which can function in various kinds of predictions, also lend themselves to retrodictive use; for example, in the dating, by means of the radiocarbon method, of a bow or an ax handle found in an archeological site.

A proposed explanation is scientifically acceptable only if its explanans is capable of empirical test, that is, roughly speaking, if it is possible to infer from it certain statements whose truth can be checked by means of suitable observational or experimental procedures. The predictive and postdictive implications of the laws invoked in a nomological explanation clearly afford an opportunity for empirical tests; the more extensive and varied the set of implications that have been borne out by empirical investigation, the better established will be the explanatory principles in question.

2. THE BASIC PATTERN OF FUNCTIONAL ANALYSIS

Historically speaking, functional analysis is a modification of teleological explanation, that is, of explanation not by reference to causes which "bring about" the event in question, but by reference to ends which determine its course. Intuitively, it seems quite plausible that a teleological approach might be required for an adequate understanding of purposive and other goal-directed behavior; and teleological explanation has always had its advocates in this context. The trouble with the idea is that in its more traditional forms, it fails to meet the minimum scientific requirement of empirical testability. The neovitalistic idea of entelechy or of vital force is a case in point. It is meant to provide an explanation for various characteristically biological phenomena, such as regeneration and regulation, which according to neovitalism cannot be explained by physical and chemical laws alone. Entelechies are conceived as goal-directed nonphysical agents which affect the course of physiological events in such a way as to restore an organism to a more or less normal state after a disturbance has occurred. However, this conception is stated in essentially metaphorical terms: no testable set of statements is provided (i) to specify the kinds of circumstances in which an entelechy will supervene as an agent directing the course of events otherwise governed by physical and chemical laws, and (ii) to indicate precisely what observable effects the action of an entelechy will have in such a case. And since neovitalism thus fails to state general laws as to when and how entelechies act, it cannot explain any biological phenomena; it can give us no grounds to expect a given phenomenon, no reasons to say: "Now we see that the phenomenon had to occur." It yields neither predictions nor retrodictions: the attribution of a biological phenomenon to the supervenience of an entelechy has no testable implications at all. This theoretical defect can be thrown into relief by contrasting the idea of entelechy with that of a magnetic field generated by an electric current, which may be invoked to explain the deflection of a magnetic needle. A magnetic field is not directly observable any more than an entelechy; but the concept is governed by strictly specifiable laws concerning the strength and direction, at any point, of the magnetic field produced by a current flowing through a given wire, and by other laws determining the effect of such a field upon a magnetic needle in the magnetic field on the earth. And it is these laws which, by their predictive and retrodictive import, confer explanatory power upon the concept of magnetic field. Teleological accounts referring to entelechies are thus seen to be pseudoexplanations. Functional analysis, as will be seen, though often worded in teleological phraseology, need not appeal to such problematic entities and has a definitely empirical core.

The kind of phenomenon that a functional analysis[4] is invoked to explain is typically some recurrent activity or some behavior pattern in an individual or a group; it may be a physiological mechanism, a neurotic trait, a culture pattern, or a social institution, for example. And the principal objective of the analysis is to exhibit the contribution which the behavior pattern makes to the preservation or the development of the individual or the group in which it occurs. Thus, functional analysis seeks to understand a behavior pattern or a sociocultural institution in terms of the role it plays in keeping the given system in proper working order and thus maintaining it as a going concern.

By way of a simple and schematized illustration, consider first the statement:

(3.1) The heartbeat in vertebrates has the function of circulating blood through the organism.

Before asking whether and how this statement might be used for explanatory purposes, we have to consider the preliminary question: what does the statement *mean*? What is being asserted by this attribution of function? It might be held that all the information conveyed by a sentence such as (3.1) can be expressed just as well by substituting

---

[4] In developing the characterization of functional analysis presented in this section, I have obtained much stimulation and information from the illuminating and richly documented essay "Manifest and Latent Functions" in R. K. Merton's book, *Social Theory and Social Structure,* revised and enlarged edition (Glencoe, Ill.: Free Press of Glencoe, Inc., 1957), pp. 19-84. Each of the passages from this work which is referred to in the present essay may also be found in the first edition (1949), on a page with approximately the same number.

the word "effect" for the word "function." But this construal would oblige us to assent also to the statement:

(3.2) The heartbeat has the function of producing heart sounds; for the heartbeat has that effect.

Yet a proponent of functional analysis would refuse to assert (3.2), on the ground that heart sounds are an effect of the heartbeat which is of no importance to the functioning of the organism; whereas the circulation of the blood effects the transportation of nutriment to, and the removal of waste from, various parts of the organism—a process that is indispensable if the organism is to remain in proper working order, and indeed if it is to stay alive. Thus understood, the import of the functional statement (3.1) might be summarized as follows:

(3.3) The heartbeat has the effect of circulating the blood, and this ensures the satisfaction of certain conditions (supply of nutriment and removal of waste) which are necessary for the proper working of the organism.

We should notice next that the heart will perform the task here attributed to it only if certain conditions are met by the organism and by its environment. For example, circulation will fail if there is a rupture of the aorta; the blood can carry oxygen only if the environment affords an adequate supply of available oxygen and the lungs are in proper condition; it will remove certain kinds of waste only if the kidneys are reasonably healthy; and so forth. Most of the conditions that would have to be specified here are usually left unmentioned, partly, no doubt, because they are assumed to be satisfied as a matter of course in situations in which the organism normally finds itself. But, in part, the omission reflects lack of relevant knowledge, for an explicit specification of the conditions in question would require a theory in which (a) the possible states of organisms and of their environments could be characterized by the values of certain physicochemical or perhaps biological "variables of state," and in which (b) the fundamental theoretical principles would permit the determination of that range of internal and external conditions within which the pulsations of the heart would perform the function referred to above.[5] At present, a general theory of this kind, or even one that could deal in this fashion with some particular kind of organism, is unavailable, of course.

---

[5] For a fuller statement and further development of this point, see part I of the essay "A Formalization of Functionalism" in E. Nagel, *Logic Without Metaphysics* (Glencoe, Ill.: Free Press of Glencoe, Inc., 1957), pp. 247-83. Part I of this essay is a detailed analytical study of Merton's essay mentioned in Note 4, and thus is of special significance for the methodology of the social sciences.

Also, a full restatement of (3.1) in the manner of (3.3) calls for criteria of what constitutes "proper working," "normal functioning," and the like, of the organism at hand; for the function of a given trait is here construed in terms of its causal relevance to the satisfaction of certain necessary conditions of proper working or survival of the organism. Here again, the requisite criteria are often left unspecified—an aspect of functional analysis whose serious implications will be considered later (in section 5).

The considerations here outlined suggest the following schematic characterization of a functional analysis:

(3.4) *Basic pattern of a functional analysis:* The object of the analysis is some "item" i, which is a relatively persistent trait or disposition (for example, the beating of the heart) occurring in a system s (for example, the body of a living vertebrate); and the analysis aims to show that s is in a state, or internal condition, c_i and in an environment presenting certain external conditions c_e such that under conditions c_i and c_e (jointly to be referred to as c) the trait i has effects which satisfy some "need" or "functional requirement" of s, that is, a condition n which is necessary for the system's remaining in adequate, or effective, or proper, working order.

Let us briefly consider some examples of this type of analysis in psychology and in sociological and anthropological studies. In psychology, it is especially psychoanalysis which shows a strong functional orientation. One clear instance is Freud's functional characterization of the role of symptom formation. In *The Problem of Anxiety*, Freud expresses himself as favoring a conception according to which "all symptom formation would be brought about solely in order to avoid anxiety; the symptoms bind the psychic energy which otherwise would be discharged as anxiety." [6] In support of this view, Freud points out that if an agoraphobic who has usually been accompanied when going out is left alone in the street, he will suffer an attack of anxiety, as will the compulsion neurotic who, having touched something, is prevented from washing his hands. "It is clear, therefore, that the stipulation of being accompanied and the compulsion to wash have as their purpose, and also their result, the averting of an outbreak of anxiety." [7] In this account, which is put in strongly teleological terms, the system s is the individual under consideration; i his agoraphobic or compulsive behavior pattern; n the binding of anxiety, which is necessary to avert a serious psychological crisis that would make it impossible for the individual to function adequately.

---

[6] S. Freud, *The Problem of Anxiety*, trans. H. A. Bunker (New York: Psychoanalytic Quarterly Press, and W. W. Norton & Company, Inc., 1936), p. 111.
[7] *Ibid.*, p. 112.

In anthropology and sociology the object of functional analysis is, in Merton's words, "a standardized (that is, patterned and repetitive) item, such as social roles, institutional patterns, social processes, cultural pattern, culturally patterned emotions, social norms, group organization, social structure, devices for social control, etc." [8] Here, as in psychology and biology, the function, that is, the stabilizing or adjusting effect, of the item under study, may be one not consciously sought (and indeed, it might not even be consciously recognized) by the agents; in this case, Merton speaks of *latent* functions—in contradistinction to *manifest* functions, that is, those stabilizing objective effects which are intended by participants in the system.[9] Thus, for example, the rainmaking ceremonials of the Hopi fail to achieve their manifest meteorological objective, but they "may fulfill the latent function of reinforcing the group identity by providing a periodic occasion on which the scattered members of a group assemble to engage in a common activity." [10]

Radcliffe-Brown's functional analysis of the totemic rites of certain Australian tribes illustrates the same point: "To discover the social function of the totemic rites we have to consider the whole body of cosmological ideas of which each rite is a partial expression. I believe that it is possible to show that the social structure of an Australian tribe is connected in a very special way with these cosmological ideas and that the maintenance of its continuity depends on keeping them alive, by their regular expression in myth and rite.

"Thus, any satisfactory study of the totemic rites of Australia must be based not simply on the consideration of their ostensible purpose . . . , but on the discovery of their meaning and of their social function." [11]

Malinowski attributes important latent functions to religion and to magic: he argues that religious faith establishes and enhances mental attitudes such as reverence for tradition, harmony with environment, and confidence and courage in critical situations and at the prospect of death—attitudes which, embodied and maintained by cult and ceremo-

[8] Merton, *op. cit.*, p. 50.

[9] *Ibid.*, p. 51. Merton defines manifest functions as those which are both intended and recognized, and latent functions as those which are neither intended nor recognized. But this characterization allows for functions which are neither manifest nor latent; for example, those which are recognized though not intended. It would seem to be more in keeping with Merton's intentions, therefore, to base the distinction simply on whether or not the stabilizing effect of the given item was deliberately sought.

[10] *Ibid.*, pp. 64-65.

[11] A. R. Radcliffe-Brown, *Structure and Function in Primitive Society* (London: Cohen and West, Ltd., 1952), p. 145.

nial, have "an immense biological value." He points out that magic, by providing man with certain ready-made rituals, techniques, and beliefs, enables him "to maintain his poise and his mental integrity in fits of anger, in the throes of hate, of unrequited love, of despair and anxiety. The function of magic is to ritualize man's optimism, to enhance his faith in the victory of hope over fear." [12]

There will soon be occasion to add to the preceding examples from psychoanalysis and anthropology some instances of functional analysis in sociology. To illustrate the general character of the procedure, however, the cases mentioned so far will suffice: they all exhibit the basic pattern outlined in (3.4). We now turn from our examination of the form of functional analysis to a scrutiny of its significance as a mode of explanation.

3. THE EXPLANATORY IMPORT OF FUNCTIONAL ANALYSIS

Functional analysis is widely considered as achieving an *explanation* of the "items" whose functions it studies. Malinowski, for example, says of the functional analysis of culture that it "aims at the explanation of anthropological facts at all levels of development by their function . . ." [13] and he adds, in the same context: "To explain any item of culture, material or moral, means to indicate its functional place within an institution, . . ." [14] At another place, Malinowski speaks of the "functional explanation of art, recreation, and public ceremonials." [15]

[12] B. Malinowski, *Magic, Science and Religion, and Other Essays* (Garden City, N.Y.: Doubleday Anchor Books, 1954), p. 90. For an illuminating comparison of Malinowski's views on the functions of magic and religion with those advanced by Radcliffe-Brown, see G. C. Homans, *The Human Group* (New York: Harcourt, Brace & World, Inc., 1950), pp. 321 ff. (Note also Homans' general comments on "the functional theory," *ibid.*, pp. 268-72.) This issue and other aspects of functional analysis in anthropology are critically examined in the following article, which confronts some specific applications of the method with programmatic declarations by its proponents: Leon J. Goldstein, "The Logic of Explanation in Malinowskian Anthropology," *Philosophy of Science*, Vol. XXIV (1957), 156-66.

[13] B. Malinowski, "Anthropology," *Encyclopaedia Britannica*, First Supplementary Volume (London and New York: The Encyclopaedia Britannica, Inc., 1926), 132.

[14] *Ibid.*, p. 139.

[15] B. Malinowski, *A Scientific Theory of Culture, and Other Essays* (Chapel Hill, N.C.: University of North Carolina Press, 1944), p. 174.

Radcliffe-Brown, too, considers functional analysis as an explanatory method, though not as the only one suited for the social sciences: "Similarly one 'explanation' of a social system will be its history, where we know it—the detailed account of how it came to be what it is and where it is. Another 'explanation' of the same system is obtained by showing (as the functionalists attempt to do) that it is a special exemplification of laws of social physiology or social functioning. The two kinds of explanation do not conflict, but supplement one another." [16]

Apart from illustrating the attribution of explanatory import to functional analysis, this passage raises two points which bear on the general question as to the nature of explanation in empirical science. We will therefore digress briefly to comment on these points.

First, as Radcliffe-Brown stresses, a functional analysis has to refer to general laws. This is shown also in our schematic characterization (3.4): the statements that i, in the specified setting c, has effects that satisfy n, and that n is a necessary condition for the proper functioning of the system, both involve general laws. For a statement of causal connection this is well known; and the assertion that a condition n constitutes a functional prerequisite for a state of some specified kind (such as proper functioning) is tantamount to the statement of a law to the effect that whenever condition n fails to be satisfied, the state in question fails to occur. Thus, explanation by functional analysis requires reference to laws.[17]

---

[16] Radcliffe-Brown, *op. cit.,* p. 186.

[17] Malinowski, at one place in his writings, endorses a pronouncement which might appear to be at variance with this conclusion: "Description cannot be separated from explanation, since in the words of a great physicist, 'explanation is nothing but condensed description.'" (Malinowski, "Anthropology," *op. cit.,* p. 132.) He seems to be referring here to the views of Ernst Mach or of Pierre Duhem, who took a similar position on this point. Mach conceived the basic objective of science as the brief and economic description of recurrent phenomena and considered laws as a highly efficient way of compressing, as it were, the description of an infinitude of potential particular occurrences into a simple and compact formula. But, thus understood, the statement approvingly quoted by Malinowski is, of course, entirely compatible with our point about the relevance of laws for functional explanation.

Besides, a law can be called a description only in a Pickwickian sense. For even so simple a generalization as "All vertebrates have hearts" does not describe any particular individual, such as Rin-Tin-Tin, as being a vertebrate and having a heart; rather, it asserts of Rin-Tin-Tin—and of any other object, whether vertebrate or not—that *if* it is a vertebrate *then* it has a heart. Thus, the generalization has the import of an indefinite set of conditional statements about particular objects. In addition, a law might be said to imply statements about "potential events" which never actually take place. The gas law, for ex-

The second point relates to a concept invoked by Radcliffe-Brown, of a historic-genetic explanation, which accounts for an item such as a social system or institution by tracing its origins. Clearly, the mere listing of a series of events preceding the given item cannot qualify as an explanation; temporal precedence does not in itself make an event relevant to the genesis of the item under consideration. Thus, a criterion of relevance is needed for the characterization of a sound historic-genetic explanation. As brief reflection shows, relevance here consists in causal or probabilistic determination. A historic-genetic explanation will normally proceed in stages, beginning with some initial set of circumstances which are said to have "brought about," or "led to," certain events at a later time; of these it is next argued that by virtue of, or in conjunction with, certain further conditions prevailing at that later time, they led to a specified further set of events in the historical development; these are in turn combined with additional factors then prevailing and lead to a still later stage, and so forth, until the final explanandum is reached. In a genetic account of this kind, the assertion that a given set of circumstances brought about certain specified subsequent conditions clearly has to be construed as claiming a nomological connection of causal, or more likely, of probabilistic, character. Thus, there is tacit reference to general laws of strictly universal or of statistical form; and a historic-genetic explanation can be construed schematically as a sequence of steps each of which has the character of a nomological explanation. However, while in each step but the first, some of the particular facts mentioned in the explanans will have been accounted for by preceding explanatory steps, the other particular facts invoked will be brought in simply by way of supplementary information. Thus, even in a highly schematic construal, a historic-genetic explanation cannot be viewed as proceeding from information about circumstances at some initial time, *via* certain statistical or causal laws alone, to the final explanandum: it is essential that, as the argument goes on, additional information is fed into it, concerning certain events which supervene "from the outside," as it were, at various stages of the process under study. Let us note that exactly the same procedure would be required in the case of the melting ice if, during the period of time under consideration, the system were subject to certain outside influences, such as someone's pushing the beaker and spilling some of the water, or salt being added to the water. Basically, then, historic-genetic explanation is nomological explanation.

Returning now to the main issue of the present section, we have to

---

ample, implies that if a given body of gas were to be heated under constant pressure at time *t*, its volume would increase. But if in fact the gas is not heated at *t* this statement can hardly be said to be a description of any particular event.

ask what explanatory import may properly be attributed to functional analysis. Suppose, then, that we are interested in explaining the occurrence of a trait i in a system s (at a certain time t), and that the following functional analysis is offered:

(4.1)

    (a) At t, s functions adequately in a setting of kind c (characterized by specific internal and external conditions)

    (b) s functions adequately in a setting of kind c only if a certain necessary condition, n, is satisfied

    (c) If trait i were present in s then, as an effect, condition n would be satisfied

    (d) (Hence,) at t, trait i is present in s

For the moment, we will leave aside the question as to what precisely is meant by statements of the types (a) and (b), and especially by the phrase "s functions adequately"; these matters will be examined in section 5. Right now, we will concern ourselves only with the *logic* of the argument; that is, we will ask whether (d) formally follows from (a), (b), (c), just as in a deductive nomological explanation the explanandum follows from the explanans. The answer is obviously in the negative, for, to put it pedantically, the argument (4.1) involves the fallacy of affirming the consequent in regard to premise (c). More explicitly, the statement (d) could be validly inferred if (c) asserted that *only* the presence of trait i could effect satisfaction of condition n. As it is, we can infer merely that condition n must be satisfied in some way or other at time t; for otherwise, by reason of (b), the system s could not be functioning adequately in its setting, in contradiction to what (a) asserts. But it might well be that the occurrence of any one of a number of alternative items would suffice no less than the occurrence of i to satisfy requirement n, in which case the account provided by the premises of (4.1) simply fails to explain why the trait i rather than one of its alternatives is present in s at t.

As has just been noted, this objection would not apply if premise (c) could be replaced by the statement that requirement n can be met *only* by the presence of trait i. And indeed, some instances of functional analysis seem to involve the claim that the specific item under analysis is, in this sense, functionally indispensable for the satisfaction of n. For example, Malinowski makes this claim for magic when he asserts that "magic fulfills an indispensable function within culture. It satisfies a definite need which cannot be satisfied by any other factors of primitive civilization," [18] and again when he says about magic that "without its power and guidance early man could not have mastered his practical difficulties as he has done, nor could man have advanced to the higher

[18] Malinowski, "Anthropology," *op. cit.,* p. 136.

stages of culture. Hence the universal occurrence of magic in primitive societies and its enormous sway. Hence we do find magic an invariable adjunct of all important activities." [19]

However, the assumption of functional indispensability for a given item is highly questionable on empirical grounds: in all concrete cases of application, there do seem to exist alternatives. For example, the binding of anxiety in a given subject might be effected by an alternative symptom, as the experience of psychiatrists seems to confirm. Similarly, the function of the rain dance might be subserved by some other group ceremonial. And interestingly, Malinowski himself, in another context, invokes "the principle of limited possibilities, first laid down by Goldenweiser. Given a definite cultural need, the means of its satisfaction are small in number, and therefore the cultural arrangement which comes into being in response to the need is determined within narrow limits." [20] This principle obviously involves at least a moderate liberalization of the conception that every cultural item is functionally indispensable. But even so, it may still be too restrictive. At any rate, sociologists such as Parsons and Merton have assumed the existence of "functional equivalents" for certain cultural items; and Merton, in his general analysis of functionalism, has insisted that the conception of the functional indispensability of cultural items be replaced quite explicitly by the assumption of "functional alternatives, or functional equivalents, or functional substitutes." [21] This idea, incidentally, has an interesting parallel in the "principle of multiple solutions" for adaptational problems in evolution. This principle, which has been emphasized by functionally oriented biologists, states that for a given functional problem (such as that of perception of light) there are usually a variety of possible solutions, and many of these are actually used by different—and often closely related—groups of organisms.[22]

It should be noted here that, in any case of functional analysis, the question whether there are functional equivalents to a given item i has a definite meaning only if the internal and external conditions c in (4.1)

[19] Malinowski, *Magic, Science and Religion, and Other Essays, op. cit.*, p. 90. (Note the explanatory claim implicit in the use of the word "hence.")

[20] B. Malinowski, "Culture," *Encyclopedia of the Social Sciences*, Vol. IV (New York: The Macmillan Company, 1931), 626.

[21] Merton, *op. cit.*, p. 34. Cf. also T. Parsons, *Essays in Sociological Theory, Pure and Applied* (Glencoe, Ill.: Free Press of Glencoe, Inc., 1949), p. 58. For an interesting recent attempt to establish the existence of functional alternatives in a specific case, see R. D. Schwartz, "Functional alternatives to inequality," *American Sociological Review*, Vol. XX (1955), 424-30.

[22] See G. G. Simpson, *The Meaning of Evolution* (New Haven, Conn.: Yale University Press, 1949), pp. 164 ff., 190, 342-43; and G. G. Simpson, C. S. Pittendrigh, L. H. Tiffany, *Life* (New York: Harcourt, Brace & World, Inc., 1957), p. 437.

are clearly specified. Otherwise, any proposed alternative to i, say i', could be denied the status of a functional equivalent on the ground that, being different from i, the item i' would have certain effects on the internal state and the environment of s which would not be brought about by i; and that therefore, if i' rather than i were realized, s would not be functioning in the same internal and external situation.

Suppose, for example, that the system of magic of a given primitive group were replaced by an extension of its rational technology plus some modification of its religion, and that the group were to continue as a going concern. Would this establish the existence of a functional equivalent to the original system of magic? A negative answer might be defended on the grounds that as a result of adopting the modified pattern the group had changed so strongly in regard to some of its basic characteristics (that is, its internal state, as characterized by c_i, had been so strongly modified) that it was not the original kind of primitive group any more; and that there simply was no functional equivalent to magic which would leave all the "essential" features of the group unimpaired. Consistent use of this type of argument would safeguard the postulate of the functional indispensability of every cultural item against any conceivable empirical disconfirmation, by turning it into a covert tautology.

Let I be the class of those items, i, i', i'', . . . , any one of which, if present in s under conditions c, would effect satisfaction of condition n. Then those items are functional equivalents in Merton's sense, and what the premises of (4.1) entitle us to infer is only:

> (4.2) Some one of the items in class I is present in s at t. But the premises give us no grounds to expect i rather than one of its functional alternatives.

So far, we have viewed functional analysis only as a presumptive deductive explanation. Might it not be construed instead as an inductive argument which shows that the occurrence of i is highly probable in the circumstances described by the premises? Might it not be possible, for example, to add to the premises of (4.1) a further statement to the effect that the functional prerequisite n can be met only by i and by a few specifiable functional alternatives? And might not these premises make the presence of i highly probable? This course is hardly promising, for in most, if not all, concrete cases it would be impossible to specify with any precision the range of alternative behavior patterns, institutions, customs, or the like that would suffice to meet a given functional prerequisite or need. And even if that range could be characterized, there is no satisfactory method in sight for dividing it into some finite number of cases and assigning a probability to each of these.

Assume, for example, that Malinowski's general view of the function of magic is correct: how are we to determine, when trying to explain the system of magic of a given group, all the different systems of magic and alternative cultural patterns any one of which would satisfy the same functional requirements for the group as does the actually existing system of magic? And how are we to ascribe probabilities of occurrence to each of these potential functional equivalents? Clearly, there is no satisfactory way of answering these questions, and practitioners of functional analysis do not claim to achieve their explanation in this extremely problematic fashion.

Nor is it any help to construe the general laws implicit in the statements (b) and (c) in (4.1) as statistical rather than strictly universal in form, that is, as expressing connections that are very probable, but do not hold universally; for the premises thus obtained would still allow for functional alternatives of i (each of which would make satisfaction of n highly probable), and thus the basic difficulty would remain: the premises taken jointly could still not be said to make the presence just of i highly probable.

In sum then, the information typically provided by a functional analysis of an item i affords neither deductively nor inductively adequate grounds for expecting i rather than one of its alternatives. The impression that a functional analysis does provide such grounds, and thus explains the occurrence of i, is no doubt at least partly due to the benefit of hindsight: when we seek to explain an item i, we presumably know already that i has occurred.

But, as was briefly noted earlier, a functional analysis provides, in principle, the basis for an explanation with a weaker explanandum; for the premises (a) and (b) of (4.1) imply the consequence that the necessary condition n must be fulfilled in some way or other. This much more modest kind of functional explanation may be schematized as follows:

(4.3)

(a) At time t, system s functions adequately in a setting of kind c

(b) s functions adequately in a setting of kind c only if condition n is satisfied

(e) Some one of the items in class I is present in s at t

This kind of inference, while sound, is rather trivial, however, except in cases where we have additional knowledge about the items contained in class I. Suppose, for example, that at time t, a certain dog (system s) is in good health in a "normal" kind of setting c which precludes the use of such devices as artificial hearts, lungs, and kidneys. Suppose further that in a setting of kind c, the dog can be in good health only if his blood circulates properly (condition n). Then schema (4.3) leads only to the conclusion that in some way or other, the blood must be kept circulating properly in the dog at t—hardly a very illuminating result. If, however, we have additional knowledge of the ways in which the blood may be kept circulating under the circumstances and if we know, for example, that the only feature that would ensure proper circulation (the only item in class I) is a properly working heart, then we may draw the much more specific conclusion that at t the dog has a properly working heart. But if we make explicit the additional knowledge here used by expressing it as a third premise, then our argument assumes a form considered earlier, namely that of a functional analysis which is of the type (4.1), except that premise (c) has been replaced by the statement that i is the *only* trait by which n can be satisfied in setting c; and, as was pointed out above, the conclusion (d) of (4.1) does follow in this case; in our case, (d) is the sentence stating that the dog has a properly working heart at t.

In general, however, additional knowledge of the kind here referred to is not available, and the explanatory import of functional analysis is then limited to the precarious role schematized in (4.3).

*   *   *

SELECTED BIBLIOGRAPHY

Anscombe, G. E. M., *Intention.* Ithaca, N.Y.: Cornell University Press, 1957.

Aristotle, *Physics*, Book II.

Ashby, W. R., *Design for a Brain.* London: Chapman & Hall, Ltd., 1952.

————, "The Nervous System as Physical Machine: With Special Reference to the Origin of Adaptive Behaviour," *Mind*, Vol. LVI (1947).

Beckner, Morton, *The Biological Way of Thought.* New York: Columbia University Press, 1959.

von Bertalanffy, Ludwig, *Problems of Life.* New York: Harper & Row, Publishers, 1960.

Broad, C. D., *Mind and its Place in Nature.* New York: Harcourt, Brace & World, Inc., 1925.

————, C. A. Mace, G. F. Stout, A. C. Ewing, "Symposium: Mechanical and Teleological Causation," *Proceedings of the Aristotelian Society,* Supp. Vol. XIV (1935).

Canfield, John V., "Teleological Explanation in Biology," *British Journal for the Philosophy of Science*, Vol. XIV (1964).

Cannon, Walter B., *The Wisdom of the Body*. New York: W. W. Norton & Company, Inc., 1939.

Cohen, Jonathan, "Teleological Explanation," *Proceedings of the Aristotelian Society*, n.s., Vol. LI (1950-51).

Cohen, M. R., *Reason and Nature*. Glencoe, Ill.: Free Press of Glencoe, Inc., 1953.

Driesch, Hans, *The Science and Philosophy of the Organism*. London: Adam and Charles Black, Ltd., 1929.

Ducasse, C. J., "Explanation, Mechanism and Teleology," *Journal of Philosophy*, Vol. XXIII (1926). Reprinted in *Readings in Philosophical Analysis*, H. Feigl and W. Sellars, eds., New York: Appleton-Century-Crofts, Inc., 1949.

Goldstein, L. J., "The Logic of Explanation in Malinowskian Anthropology," *Philosophy of Science,* Vol. XXIV (1957).

Hempel, Carl G. and P. Oppenheim, "Studies in the Logic of Explanation," *Philosophy of Science*, Vol. XV (1948). Reprinted in part in *Readings in the Philosophy of Science*, H. Feigl and M. Brodbeck, eds., New York: Appleton-Century-Crofts, Inc., 1953.

MacKay, D. M., "Mind-like Behaviour in Artifacts," *British Journal for the Philosophy of Science,* Vol. II (1951).

Merton, R. K., "Manifest and Latent Functions," in *Social Theory and Social Structure,* Glencoe, Ill.: Free Press of Glencoe, Inc., 1957.

Nagel, E., "Concept and Theory Formation in the Social Sciences." Reprinted in J. L. Jarret and S. M. McMurrin, eds., *Contemporary Philosophy,* New York: Holt, Rinehart & Winston, Inc., 1954.

Peters, R. S., *The Concept of Motivation*. London: Routledge & Kegan Paul Ltd., 1958.

Peters, R. S., J. McCrackon, J. O. Urmson, "Symposium: Motives and Causes," *Proceedings of the Aristotelian Society*, Supp. Vol. XXVII (1952).

Rigano, E., "The Concept of Purpose in Biology," *Mind,* n.s., Vol. XL (1931).

Russell, Bertrand, *The Analysis of Mind*, Ch. 3. New York: The Macmillan Company, 1921.

Russell, E. S., *The Directiveness of Organic Activities*. Cambridge, Eng.: Cambridge University Press, 1945.

Sommerhoff, G., *Analytical Biology*. London: Oxford University Press, 1950.

Sorabji, Richard, "Function," *Philosophical Quarterly*, Vol. XIV (1964).

Taylor, Richard, "Purposeful and Non-Purposeful Behavior: A Rejoinder," *Philosophy of Science*, Vol. XVII (1950).

Wiener, N., *Cybernetics*. New York: M.I.T. Press, 1961.

Wisdom, J. O., "The Hypothesis of Cybernetics," *British Journal for the Philosophy of Science,* Vol. II (1951).

————, R. J. Spilsbury, D. M. MacKay, "Symposium: Mentality in Machines," *Proceedings of the Aristotelian Society,* Supp. Vol. XXVI (1952).

Woodger, J. H., *Biological Principles*. New York: Harcourt, Brace & World, Inc., 1929.

127   5   207

80